# The safe isolation of plant and equipment

HSE Books

*First published 1997*
*Second edition 2006*

ISBN 0 7176 6171 7



This guidance is issued by the Health and Safety Executive. Following the guidance is not compulsory and you are free to take other action. But if you do follow the guidance you will normally be doing enough to comply with the law. Health and safety inspectors seek to secure compliance with the law and may refer to this guidance as illustrating good practice.

# Contents

# Foreword

Failures during the isolation and reinstatement of process plant are one of the main causes of loss-of-containment incidents, and may lead to major accidents. High standards of isolation and rigorous management control are required for plant isolation and reinstatement, particularly in major hazard industries.

This guidance reflects current industry 'good practice' standards. It has been developed by a joint working group, including members from industry, trade unions and the Health and Safety Executive. It replaces the Oil Industry Advisory Committee's 1997 document *The safe isolation of plant and equipment* (ISBN 0 7176 0871 9).

This revised guidance reflects our increased appreciation of the importance of human factors in safe isolations. Analysis confirms that where incidents occur, the root causes often include human failures.

We recommend the review of company procedures against the principles and practical guidance contained in this publication. An action plan should then be prepared for the implementation of any necessary improvements.

Effective and lasting improvement can be achieved where all concerned, from senior management to those carrying out work on the plant, share a genuine commitment to achieving and maintaining isolation procedures of a high standard.

We would like to thank the following individuals, their employers and industry groups for their contribution.

| | | |
|---|---|---|
| Ian Darlington | Shell UK Oil Products | UKPIA |
| Kevin Dixon-Jackson* | CIBA Speciality Chemicals plc | CIA |
| Martyn Foote | Cresent | UKOOA |
| Stuart Kennedy | National Grid | UKOOA |
| Peter Thompson | BP Exploration Operating Company Ltd | UKOOA |
| Ron Wood* | Shell UK Oil Products | TGWU |
| Mike Young | Petrofac Facilities Management | UKOOA |

*CDOIF member

# Introduction

## Scope and target audience

1 This publication provides guidance on the general principles of safe process isolations. It describes how to isolate plant and equipment safely, and how to reduce the risk of releasing hazardous substances during intrusive activities such as maintenance and sampling operations.

2 It includes a methodology for selecting 'baseline' process isolation standards and outlines preventive and mitigatory risk reduction measures. It is intended for use as a reference to assist duty holders to develop, review and enhance their own isolation standards and procedures.

3 The guidance applies to the following industries:

- the onshore and offshore oil and gas industry;
- chemical manufacturing; and
- pipelines associated with these industries.

It also has general application to all industries where process isolations are made, and applies to mobile offshore drilling units where relevant (eg well test facilities, underbalanced drilling etc).

4 This guidance is primarily intended for senior operational managers who are responsible for their companies' isolations systems, and for the health and safety professionals who advise them. It will also be of interest to employee representatives and to anyone who monitors, audits and reviews isolations systems. Organisations responsible for the design and modification of plant should use this guidance to ensure that their designs provide adequate isolation facilities.

5 Key issues for this guidance include:

- the importance of good design (for new plant **and** for plant modifications);
- the critical role of human factors in preventing loss of containment;
- a revised and recalibrated selection tool;
- plant reinstatement as a critical element of isolation activity;
- guidance on the use of 'variations' from company standards;
- advice on controlling own isolations and extended term isolations; and
- the inclusion of medium and low pressure gas distribution networks within the scope of the document.

6 The guidance is intended to reflect industry **'good practice'** for the design of new plant. It applies to existing plant to the extent that it is reasonably practicable to do so. Any alterations required to reduce risks for **existing plant** to 'as low as reasonably practicable' (see paragraphs 13-16) should be identified and carried out within an appropriate timescale.

7 The primary concern of this guidance is with **process isolations** eg for intrusive maintenance on live plant. The principles are also relevant for non-intrusive isolations that involve breaking the containment envelope and for controlling long-term process plant configurations. The guidance is not intended for emergency situations where loss of containment has occurred and immediate isolation of inventory is required. It does not apply to non-process plant and equipment (eg powered access equipment used during isolation activities).

8 The main focus is on **risks to the safety of people**, particularly where activities present potential major accident hazards. Avoiding loss of containment will also improve environmental protection and reduce business interruption.

9 The effectiveness of an isolation system depends on the adequacy of other arrangements, including work control systems (especially permit-to-work), operating procedures, training and competence, management of change and contingency plans. The *References and further reading* section gives sources of more detailed guidance on such topics.

*Terms 'should', 'may' and 'must'*

10 Throughout this publication, verbs with specific meanings are used:

- **should** – primary verb for statements of guidance;
- **may** – where the guidance suggests options; and
- **must** – only where there is a specific legal/statutory requirement for the measures described, or where the dangers of not taking that course of action are self-evident.

## Legal considerations

11 Relevant legislation is listed in Appendix 1.

*Contractors and subcontractors*
12 The client company is responsible for operational health and safety, irrespective of where its resources come from – whether its own staff, contract, subcontract or agency staff or self-employed workers. Duties in relation to contract staff (eg training, provision of information, co-operation between employers) are further discussed in *Management of health and safety at work*.[1]

## Risk reduction and 'as low as reasonably practicable' (ALARP)

13 The Health and Safety at Work etc Act 1974, and associated legislation, requires duty holders to reduce risk, **so far as is reasonably practicable**. The qualification **as low as reasonably practicable** (ALARP), which has been used throughout this document, is interpreted in the same way.

14 To show that you have reduced risks to this level, you must identify the risk reduction measures available and determine the level of risk reduction that can be achieved and the associated cost. Unless the sacrifice involved in implementing the risk reduction measure is **grossly disproportionate** to the benefits of the risk reduction, then you must implement the measure. Where available measures are not taken, you must justify this decision.

15 The greater the potential hazard, the more effective, secure and controlled the isolation should be. Where a number of options for risk reduction exist, you must use the lowest-risk option that is reasonably practicable. Engineering solutions are preferred to procedural controls or to reliance on the use of personal protective equipment (PPE).

16 In some circumstances, the risks associated with an isolation may be **intolerable**.[2] In such cases the work **should not go ahead**. No individual step in an isolation procedure should be associated with an intolerable risk. Instead, you should find an alternative approach (eg plant shutdown) that does not involve intolerable risk. This guidance does not attempt to define a criterion for isolations of intolerable risk. These will be situation-specific.

## Overview of isolation hazards

17 Oil refineries, oil and gas production installations and chemical processing plants are characterised by long lengths of continuously welded pipework and pipelines connecting process vessels, plant and installations. The contents are often hazardous substances, which may be flammable and/or toxic and are often at high temperatures and/or pressures.

18 Any intrusive activity could allow the escape of hazardous substances. The implementation of adequate isolation practices is critical to avoiding loss of containment. You should minimise isolation requirements, wherever practicable, by planning intrusive maintenance for shutdown periods. When maintenance work has to be carried out on live plant a high standard of management will be required.

19 Release of hazardous substances due to inadequate process isolation may lead to:

- local immediate effects to people (death or injury) and to the environment. Long-term effects to people and the environment may be equally serious; and/or
- escalation of the initial release, causing wider damage to plant and other systems (eg damage resulting in further releases of inventory).

20 This guidance is focused mainly on loss of containment hazards, but personal injury hazards and non-process isolation hazards should also be considered (see Appendix 2). These include:

- mechanical equipment;
- electrical equipment (including process control systems);
- hazardous atmospheres in confined spaces; and
- special hazards such as radioactive sources and static electricity.

21 Plant reinstatement is a critical aspect of any intrusive activity. Incorrect or incomplete reinstatement is likely to result in loss of containment.

# Management of isolations

## Basic principles

22 The requirements for risk management are discussed in *Management of health and safety at work*.[1] The basic principles are to:

- avoid risk wherever possible;
- carry out risk assessment to evaluate risks that cannot be avoided;
- take action to reduce risks to ALARP levels; and
- reduce risks at source wherever possible.

23 The HSE publication *Successful health and safety management*[3] describes the principles and management practice that provide a framework for effective management of health and safety.

24 This guidance sets out expectations for managing isolations activities, ie that you:

- set a policy and standards for isolation activities, to reduce risk to ALARP;
- set procedures/processes, with worker participation, to achieve secure isolations in normal operating conditions and in other foreseeable conditions;
- assess any proposed deviations from company procedures, authorise these at an appropriate level and record/monitor them;
- monitor and periodically audit your isolations procedures and use that information in the review of your isolations policy (a checklist for reviewing the adequacy of the overall arrangements is given at Appendix 3); and
- have, for multi-site operations, an element of corporate oversight[4] in standard-setting and assurance (for example, central reporting of objective information on the performance of isolations systems).

25 The potential for **human failure** during isolations, and its importance, is discussed in paragraphs 42-46. It is important that you both understand and act upon this knowledge. Critical aspects of people's role within isolations systems include:

- setting roles and responsibilities for key personnel;
- training, competence and authorisation; and
- the management activities of monitoring, audit and review and then **taking action**.

## Design

*Principles*

26 Good design maximises inherent safety and is fundamental to achieving safe and effective isolation without placing unnecessary constraints on plant operation. Some intrusive maintenance or internal inspection tasks will always require plant shutdown. Where isolation to enable intrusive activities is appropriate, suitable isolation arrangements on the plant should be clearly specified at the design stage.

27 The opportunity to achieve an inherently safer design is greatest for new plant and equipment. **Wherever reasonably practicable**, the same approach should be followed for plant modifications (see paragraphs 137-140).

28 The potential for human failure, including error, should be addressed and, wherever possible, minimised in the design.

29 At an early point in the design process the client should specify the intentions for normal and alternative mode(s) of operation, sparing of equipment, and the equipment maintenance strategy. Where possible, this should anticipate the intended lifecycle of the plant, including foreseeable modifications (for example addition of equipment). This philosophy should be documented and will determine the plant's outline isolation requirements. Any proposed deviation from the agreed design basis once the plant is operational should be justified through risk assessment before alternative isolation arrangements are used.

30 The following issues should be considered and included within the design documentation:

- alternative modes of plant operation using differing flow routes;
- requirements for intrusive plant operations (for example filter change-out, sampling or removal of pipeline pigs from launchers and receivers) and requirements for access into equipment for inspection and/or maintenance; and
- the detail of isolation arrangements, including valve types, spacers/spading points or spectacle blinds, test points and associated vents and drains for venting, flushing and purging.

*Positive isolation requirements*

31 Design of new plant should include facilities for **positive isolation** (including the valved isolation to install the positive isolation) in the following situations:

- for vessel entry, where a requirement for entry cannot be eliminated by equipment design (see paragraph 97);
- for isolation of toxic fluids; or
- to control segregation of parts of the plant which, in alternative operating modes, might otherwise be exposed to overpressure conditions. This applies where it is not reasonably practicable for the installed safety systems to protect all foreseeable operating configurations, for example the separation of a high-pressure plant from its drainage system.

*Plant Identification*

32 A scheme to uniquely identify all process plant, piping, and valves should be drawn up. All items should be readily identifiable on the plant and referenced on the piping and instrumentation diagrams (P&IDs). In addition, you should **permanently label** key items of equipment. Formal, simple, easily visible and unambiguous labelling should be provided wherever mistakes in identification could occur and could result in significant consequences.[5, 6]

*Pipework*

33 Pipework layout should minimise trapped inventories and allow easy removal of fluid for isolation purposes. Ensure that pipework:

- is of sufficient size and design to minimise the possibility of becoming blocked in service; and
- is robust and able, where appropriate, to cope with the repetitive stresses imposed by vibration, pulsating pressure and temperature cycling.[7]

34 Any piece of pipework intended for physical disconnection should be easily removable. Pipework supports should provide adequate support during disconnection. Provide supports where temporary hoses will be required for bleeding.

*Valves*

35 Specify suitable isolation valves for the service fluid and operating conditions (see Appendix 4). Ensure that you can **indicate** and **effectively secure** the position of manually operated valves.

*Pressure safety valves*

36 Isolation valves should be provided downstream of pressure safety valves for safe isolation from a shared flare or vent system if intrusive maintenance is intended at any time when the remainder of the flare or vent system is in operation. Also, where an isolation valve is downstream from a pressure safety valve, you should be able to secure the isolation valve in the open position at all times when the pressure safety valve is on-line. Standards for safety systems in unfired pressure vessels are given in BS EN 764-7.[8]

37 Where pressure safety valves are spared and continued plant operation is intended, suitable isolation facilities must also be provided upstream of the pressure safety valves. Appropriate arrangements are required to ensure that the isolation valves do not impair the performance of the pressure safety valves in service, and that closure of the downstream isolation valve does not expose pipework downstream of the off-line pressure safety valve to over-pressure from the live plant.

*Spared equipment*

38 For spared or parallel-operated equipment, isolation arrangements should allow complete segregation from on-line equipment for operational and/or maintenance reasons. The arrangements should also provide for operational/maintenance requirements of associated shared services, including control systems and fluid disposal systems such as flare headers.

*Location of isolation and testing facilities*

39 Unless risk assessment indicates otherwise, isolation and bleed points should be as close as possible to the plant item. Concentration of maintenance work in one place aids control of the isolation arrangements and minimises the inventory of fluid to be depressurised/drained. Ensure that bleeds are:

- arranged so that their discharge cannot harm personnel or plant, and toxic or flammable material can be conveyed to a safe place for disposal; and
- easily accessible for checking.

40 For every isolation point, the design should provide for facilities to test and to monitor the integrity of the isolation, eg valved connections for installation of temporary equipment such as pressure gauges.

**An example**

A filter cage was being removed for cleaning from a horizontal in-line filter. This was located on a distribution leg off the main, served by 14 mixers. The filter was isolated on each side, then the front of the unit was opened to remove the filter cage. A significant quantity of highly flammable liquid was lost through the open filter box door. The upstream gate valve was passing – it had not closed fully because of a partial blockage.

*This isolation did not have adequate provision for testing, ie no vent/drain and no means of monitoring pressure. Isolation procedures should specify testing and monitoring requirements.*

*Access and lighting*

41 Your design should enable suitable access to, and lighting of, all isolation points and associated items. Where spades need to be inserted or where sections of plant or pipework need to be removed, lifting beams suitable for attachment of portable lifting appliances, or access for cranes, should be provided.

## Human factors

42 Incident analysis confirms that human failures cause, or are involved in, a large proportion of isolation failures. The performance of isolations depends not only on the integrity of the isolation hardware, but also on the adequacy of the

arrangements for identifying each isolation point, securing the isolation, proving/monitoring and maintaining overall control of work. Human failures are discussed in detail in *Reducing error and influencing behaviour*.[9]

43 Human failures can be grouped into errors and violations.

- A human **error** is an action or decision, which was **not intended**, which involved a deviation from an accepted standard, and which led to an adverse outcome.
- A **violation** is a **deliberate** deviation from a rule or procedure and usually arises because of a desire to carry out the job despite barriers such as work or time pressures, lack of staff, unavailability of the right equipment or tools, and/or extreme weather conditions.

44 Examples of human failures relevant to isolation include:

- failure to complete or reverse isolations fully before starting work or restarting plant;
- failure to prove and monitor isolated valves;
- poor communication (eg at shift handover); and
- failure to check P&IDs/schematic diagrams against the actual installed plant and equipment.

**An example**

A valve and vent line had been used to verify mechanical isolations made on a 30 cm gas line during maintenance. The valve had been left in the open position. When the system was pressurised, a gas leak resulted.

*The appropriate position for vent valves during intrusive work is indicated by risk assessment. Correct reinstatement is critical. The worksite should be inspected prior to reinstatement, and a sample of such isolation work should be monitored by an independent person.*

45 **Competency** is a key contributor to safe isolations. Competent workers are less prone to human failures. However, even experienced and trained staff, familiar with a site, may make errors. Further training alone may not address the root causes of such error. Training and competence for isolation activities are further discussed in paragraphs 49-57.

46 Examples of isolation-specific controls that make failures less likely, and help to detect and correct them, include:

**For errors**

- Establishing and maintaining adequate understanding of hazards and the integrity of isolation arrangements.
- Providing well-designed, clear, concise, available, up-to-date procedures and instructions, including checklists and other job aids, that are accepted and used by the workforce.
- Clear identification of plant and equipment, including valves.
- A clear system for tagging valves, and recording on P&IDs and schematic diagrams.
- Providing good access (eg for valves) and working environment (eg lighting), for isolation tasks.
- Effective checking (independent where necessary) and supervision for isolation proving and monitoring, and for reinstatement.
- Good communications (eg at shift handover).
- Considering the potential for human error in risk assessments and incident investigations.

**For violations**

- Establishing a positive safety and organisational culture, with clear expectations and good reporting systems for recognising and acting on work pressures.
- Planning realistic work schedules – including managing competing demands eg between maintenance and operation, contract work and operation, shutdown modifications and maintenance – and providing adequate resources for the work.
- Well-designed isolation tasks.
- Good staff understanding of the reason for procedures and instructions and their roles and responsibilities within the system.
- Workforce participation in drawing up procedures and instructions.
- Effective supervision.
- Compliance checking eg procedural compliance audits, performance monitoring (including routine tasks).

**An example**

A confined space entry was carried out, to enable alignment of an agitator. The reactor had been cleaned and all reactor-associated lines tagged and isolated by disconnection, blanking or by double-valved isolation – except the glass vapour line to the condenser, which could not be blanked. A nitrogen line feeding into the condenser had been overlooked, and was not tagged or disconnected. An automatic valve in the line prevented nitrogen flow at this stage. The system was purged and checked for levels of oxygen and combustible gases. An entry permit was issued, and signed by all involved parties (operating, maintenance and safety personnel), following company procedures.

When the reactor top was removed, the automatic valve in the nitrogen line opened. Nitrogen flowed through the condenser and into the reactor via the vapour line. Following replacement of the reactor lid, the nitrogen concentration within the reactor then built up. The oxygen level within the reactor was not rechecked before the maintenance man entered to align the agitator. He fell as a result of partial asphyxiation and was seriously injured.

*Confined space entry requires stringent planning and extraordinary measures, as even short exposure to asphyxiants, and/or toxic chemicals can be fatal. Double-valved isolation is not adequate for vessel entry purposes.*

*A thorough examination of P&IDs and the worksite should have revealed the nitrogen supply. This should have been physically disconnected and recorded on the isolation documentation. Vessel entry requires adequate ventilation (eg forced ventilation) and lighting. The vessel atmosphere should have been retested immediately before entry. The electrical supply to the agitator should be locked out, and the agitator chocked to prevent rotation. The chock should be recorded on the isolation documentation to ensure removal prior to plant reinstatement.*

## Roles and responsibilities

47 Allocate clearly defined roles and responsibilities for drawing up, maintaining, monitoring and improving your isolations system. The responsibilities of key personnel are detailed in Figure 1.

**Figure 1:** Responsibilities of key personnel

**People in *senior management* roles** are responsible for the company's isolation policy, in particular that they:

- offer visible leadership and commitment;
- resource the development, implementation and review of the policy;
- review significant (negative and positive) results of audits;
- resource necessary remedial actions and plant modifications.

**People in *management* roles (eg plant managers, offshore installation managers (OIMs))** are responsible for ensuring that the company's isolation policy is fully implemented, in particular that:

- they define and populate an organisational structure that delivers the isolations policy;
- procedures and systems documentation are created and maintained to deliver the isolations policy;
- people are appointed to formally authorise deviations from the isolations procedures;
- plant and equipment necessary to comply with the procedures is available;
- everyone has the necessary level of competency and there are adequate supervision arrangements;
- monitoring, auditing and review is undertaken and specialist advice is sought as and when required;
- remedial actions and necessary plant modifications are implemented.

**People in *supervisory* roles (eg lead technicians)** are responsible for ensuring that the company's isolation policy is fully implemented at the plant level, in particular that:

- the isolation procedures are fully understood and followed by everyone;
- isolations of the appropriate quality are consistently delivered on the plant;
- variations from isolation standards are authorised at the appropriate level before proceeding;
- isolation and de-isolation work is adequately planned and undertaken via the permit-to-work scheme;
- information is effectively communicated between all parties;
- systems documentation in use is accurate and current;
- tasks are undertaken by competent persons;
- they adequately supervise tasks;
- planned monitoring of the system is carried out and corrective action is taken.

**People who *work on the plant* (eg operators, maintenance technicians)** are responsible for carrying out work in accordance with plant policy on isolation, in particular that they:

- understand and work to the procedures;
- work within the permit-to-work system and the planning documentation;
- will not proceed with a variation from normal procedures without proper authorisation;
- adequately identify, test and secure isolations;
- co-operate with supervisors to ensure that the policy is effectively implemented;
- communicate effectively with other parties involved in the work.

48 These safety-critical activities for isolations are an integral part of the roles and responsibilities of teams and individuals. They are primarily assured via operating discipline and supervisory arrangements. Performance standards should be defined – for example a requirement to test and prove the security of every isolation point before intrusive work goes ahead, or that induction arrangements ensure contractors' understanding of site isolation standards and procedures.

## Training and competence

49 All personnel involved in the isolation of plant and equipment should be competent to carry out their responsibilities. They should:

- understand the purpose, principles and practices of isolation procedures and safety rules – for their own role, and for others involved in the operation of isolations systems; and
- be aware of the site's major accident hazards, ie the potential consequences of any release of hazardous substances.

50 Figure 2 shows competences associated with isolation activities. The required level of competence is determined by the individual's role. You should consider those who:

- plan isolations;
- authorise isolations;
- authorise variations (or any other non-standard isolations);
- install and remove isolations; and
- work on the plant.

**Figure 2:** Competences for isolation activities

**Hazards**
- A general awareness of the hazards represented by the plant.
- A detailed understanding of the hazards on the plant and from adjacent plant.

**Documentation**
- Understand the P&IDs, loop diagrams, cause and effect diagrams and power supplies applicable to the isolation.

**PTW (permit-to-work)**
- Understand the system of PTW and isolation certificates in use.
- Know the procedures for issuing PTW and for identifying what isolations are required.
- Certified as a permit issuer.

**Isolation procedures**
- Good working knowledge of isolation and risk assessment procedures for plant.
- Understand the importance of following procedures.
- Know how to check what isolations are in place and that they are the correct isolations required.
- Know the procedures for installing/removing isolations.
- Know the procedures for draining, venting, purging and flushing.
- Know how to test and confirm correct installation of isolations.
- Know how to record isolations on an isolation certificate.
- Be able to assess the risks from non-standard isolations.

51 The achievement and maintenance of these competences should be managed via a competency assessment process. Managers who oversee and operate the competence management system play a key role. They should be competent in the areas of management, technical issues and health and safety.

52 You should respond to organisational change or to changes in systems of work via training, briefings and reassessment, as appropriate. Periodic refresher training to maintain competence will be appropriate, particularly for any safety-critical tasks that are done only rarely (for example the use of a non-standard isolation technique). This may take the form of a 'walkthrough' rehearsal of the task.

53 A comprehensive, structured training and development programme should be in place to provide both initial and refresher training. The extent of training and assessment should align with the person's role in isolations and the overarching work control arrangements, especially the site's permit-to-work systems (Further information on training and competence in relation to permit-to-work systems is contained in *Guidance on permit-to-work systems).*[10] Training and assessment should cover:

- company procedures, and roles and responsibilities;
- risk assessment, particularly for those authorised to approve 'variations' (see paragraphs 128-140);
- familiarity with relevant company, industry and regulatory guidance material; and
- awareness of legal requirements.

54 Training is likely to include site familiarisation and on-the-job training. Group training and exercises will help to ensure understanding of the interactions of roles within the overall system. Site-specific training ensures that theoretical knowledge can be successfully applied. You should consider whether safe working also requires further specific training and assessment (eg manual handling,[11] COSHH).[12]

55 Keep formal records of all training and assessment. This enables verification and audit of training and competence, and assists in identifying individuals' initial and refresher training needs.

56 Training should include assessment of performance against a standard. Demonstration of competence may involve direct and indirect observation, written records, logbooks and practical and written tests. Wherever possible, the emphasis should be on workplace assessment (for example, competency assessment for isolating authorities should involve completion of assigned field assessments in process/mechanical isolation practices and documentation).

57 Everyone who specifies and/or carries out the isolation of plant and equipment should have proven competency within their defined role before being authorised to act as isolating authorities and signatories to isolation documentation. A 'competent persons' register should be available.

## Monitoring, audit and review

58 Monitoring, audit and review enables an organisation to confirm that it **actually** does what it **says** it does, and that this is what it **should** do.

59 Effective monitoring, audit and review systems:

- find deficiencies in isolations systems and drive corrective action before these lead to losses and incidents;
- provide an objective picture of how well isolations are controlled on a site;
- are not restricted to periodic reviews, but can also **react** to incidents (on site, lessons from relevant industry accidents) and to proposed organisational change;
- should include workers' views/participation; and
- drive improvement and facilitate learning lessons and maintaining corporate memory.

60 No single monitoring, audit and review activity can capture the whole picture. In practice, a mixture of different activities is necessary. These should be appropriately resourced, based on the scale, nature, and distribution of hazards of the organisation's isolations activities.

61 Monitoring and audit procedures should cover the scope, frequencies, sampling strategy, responsibilities/competences and mechanisms for reporting results. The programme might include:

- regular compliance checks by an operator and a site manager;
- specialist audits, which assess, independently of operational management, the implementation of local procedures against corporate standards; and
- formal periodic review.

62 A full range of isolations should be examined, including:

- isolations controlled by permit and by procedures, including 'own isolations';
- routine isolations, non-standard isolations and 'variations'; and
- activities where the potential for human error could lead to serious consequences.

63 Various degrees of scrutiny may be needed, requiring different defined competences. For example, examination of risk assessment (RA) processes for isolations could include:

- compliance checks that a record of RA is available, signed/authorised at correct seniority; and/or
- a technical audit, based on a sample of high consequence isolations, which examines the adequacy of the RA conclusion (ie have risks been reduced to ALARP?)

64 Valuable information on the performance of isolations systems can come from other monitoring and audit activity (eg PTW system checks, audits of competence assurance programmes).

65 Checklists/forms can be useful tools for:

- planning and initiating remedial action; and
- periodic analysis to identify common issues which reveal underlying weaknesses in the systems.

66 Appendix 3 contains 'model' checklists, which can be tailored to a company's own arrangements:

- for site checks ('compliance monitoring') of isolation schemes; and
- to guide a review of the adequacy of isolations arrangements.

## Setting performance indicators for isolations activities

67 Setting targets against relevant numerical/other performance indicators may be part of the toolkit for managing health and safety performance.

68 Examples of performance indicators may include:

- an overall performance standard to reduce the risk of loss of containment (LoC) during isolations activities to ALARP (eg N% reduction in LoC attributable to failures in isolations activities);
- reporting, to a senior manager, the number of extended-term isolations in place (rather than modification of plant); and
- audit outcomes – number of violations against procedures.

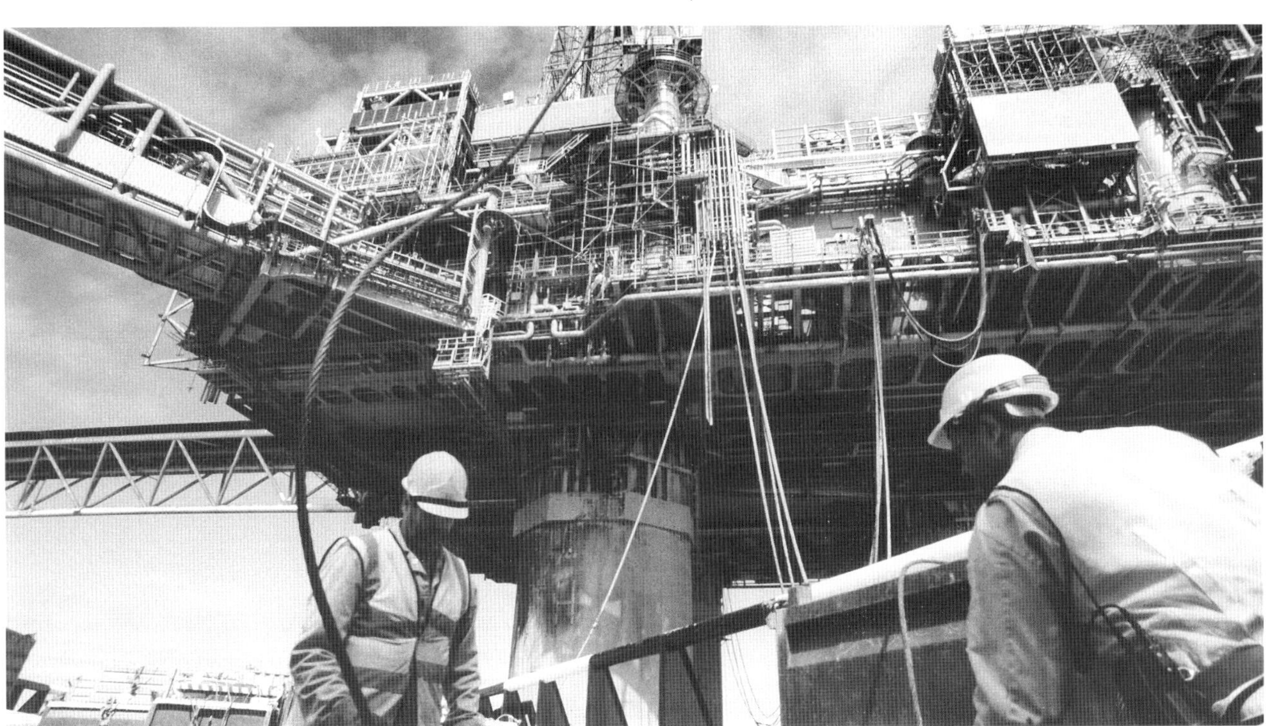

# Safe systems of work for isolation activities

## Work control systems

*Permit-to-work*

69 Permit-to-work (PTW) systems are used within safe systems of work to authorise work of a hazardous or non-routine nature on a plant. Control of isolations is normally part of a PTW system. Comprehensive guidance has been published by HSE in *Guidance on permit-to-work systems*.[10]

*Controlling work by procedures*

70 For defined categories of less hazardous work of a 'routine' nature, authorisation via operating procedures/work instructions may be acceptable. For this purpose, you should interpret 'routine' with caution and its meaning should be carefully and unambiguously defined and recorded in procedures. Procedural control of isolation activity is likely to be appropriate only for **'own isolations'** (see paragraphs 189-196). The requirements detailed in paragraph 195 will apply to all isolations carried out under procedural control.

## Documentation

*Sources of information*

71 Company standards, procedures and reference information should be accessible to all relevant workers (including short-term contractors) involved in planning and conducting the work.

72 Accurate reference information, kept updated to all plant modifications, is necessary for planning and implementing isolations. This includes:

- piping and instrumentation diagrams (P&IDs);
- process system schematics – unlike a P&ID these provide an overall view of the plant;
- piping general arrangements and/or piping isometrics;
- cause and effect diagrams; and
- loop diagrams.

73 A 'library' of standard isolations schemes for frequently used isolations may be developed and maintained. These schemes should be reviewed on **every** occasion that they are used.

*Paper 'tools' – drawings, procedures, isolation certificates, work packs, etc*

74 For all but the simplest plant, isolations should be checked against the current P&ID for the plant and marked on a suitable copy of the P&ID. If the current P&ID does not match the installation, the isolation requirements should be reassessed and confirmed on a corrected P&ID, and the schematic should be formally revised and reissued at the earliest opportunity (note that you should also consider whether this indicates a need to confirm the accuracy of other P&IDs). Process system schematics can be useful to identify the actual location, within a system, of the areas to be isolated.

75 You should use appropriate documentation, for example isolation certificates, to manage isolations safely. Isolation certificates support a safe isolation procedure by documenting the status of specified isolations. They can be used as part of a PTW system, for example where the isolation work required is not detailed on the PTW itself. Certificates should be designed for ease of understanding and use, and to support the main permit. Certificates and permits should be cross-referenced.

76 A certificate may show more than one isolation. It will often be clearer if separate certificates are used for different isolation disciplines (eg mechanical, process, electrical, and inhibits of control and safety systems). The key issue is to enable effective communication, avoiding misunderstanding or confusion.

77 Isolation certificates should allow for more than one person performing isolations within the same discipline. If separate isolation certificates are issued to cover different disciplines, they should be cross-referenced and closely co-ordinated. This is particularly important where sequencing is safety-critical. Competent people of the relevant disciplines should cross-check the certificates to ensure that all isolation requirements and standards are met.

78 Work packs can bring together documentation that relates to the whole work task in a useable form for the work party and for those who are controlling and co-ordinating the work.

79 Records of work documents (risk assessment records, method statements, permits, isolation certificates, etc) should be maintained on site for a specified time after completion and then archived, to enable effective monitoring, audit and review of the isolations systems.

## Controlling interactions with other work/systems

80 Effective communication at all levels and between all parties is required, particularly at shift handovers. On most plants, handover will be part of the PTW system and/or shift handover logbooks.

81 Your controls should ensure that isolations are not removed until the plant is in a safe condition. Robust co-ordination and control of isolations is required when separate work groups rely upon a common isolation, especially where workers are remote from any of the isolation points. This should be administered via the permit-to-work system and controlled by multi-tagging and multi-securing arrangements.

82 In areas with multiple responsibility, you should ensure adequate control, security, monitoring and communication to maintain the integrity of isolations. This may be relevant:

- where the isolation envelope involves long sections of pipeline and the isolation points are remote from the actual work area and normally controlled by other parties; and
- within a plant, where responsibility for a piece of equipment and for the location of that equipment lie with different departments/sections.

## Controlling changes

83 Reasons for change to the planned isolation scheme include:

- changes imposed by the condition of the plant (eg where a valve is stuck open, the specified depressurisation and purging cannot be achieved, or the testing of an isolation scheme gives an unsatisfactory result);
- changes to the scope of intrusive work as the work proceeds. The adequacy of the original isolation scheme must then be reconfirmed as part of the reassessment of the new work scope. This may require suspension of the work and controlling permits until the reassessment is done and the revised isolation scheme installed. The work control permit should then be revalidated or a new permit issued;
- inability to complete a job (eg due to an increase in the scope of work once it is underway, or the non-availability of spares). The adequacy of the isolation scheme over a longer duration should then be reviewed. Where appropriate, long-term standard isolations should be installed or, if safe to do so, the plant reinstated and the intrusive work reprogrammed; or
- a change in the system pressure, eg where isolation has been applied under shutdown (depressurised) conditions and plant reinstatement is proposed which will increase the system pressure to levels greater than the isolation envelope can withstand.

84 Any change to isolation arrangements should be **reviewed, reassessed** and **authorised**. The modified scheme should be captured in the work control documents (eg isolation certificates and P&IDs) to ensure full reinstatement at the end of the job.

**An example**

An operator was carrying out a routine pigging operation. On conclusion of the interlock sequence he opened the telltale bleed valve to ensure that the launcher was free of toxic and flammable gases. The gas test was negative. He then realised that he had omitted part of the procedure, requiring the interspace between the kicker line isolation valve and the pipeline isolation valves to be vented to flare. This procedure is normally carried out at the beginning of the operation. He opened the kicker line isolation valves and the pipeline isolation valves without closing the telltale door. This caused a gas release from the telltale bleed valve.

*If a process isolation deviates from the plan, whether controlled by permit-to-work or operating procedure – STOP! Re-evaluate the task. In this case, the interlock arrangements which permitted the human error to occur should be reviewed with a view to modification.*

*Sanction to test*

85 A sequence of changes in isolation status will arise from various testing requirements. You may need to temporarily reverse elements of an isolation scheme to confirm that work stages have been correctly completed (eg temporary reinstatement of the power supply to a fan motor to confirm correct direction of rotation). Typically, approval for 'sanction to test' is required at the intermediate stage of a work activity involving equipment function checks and or pre-start tests. These requirements must be implemented via the controlling documentation such as work permits and task risk assessments. You should **not** authorise/use sanction to test where isolation removal would permit reintroduction of the hazardous fluid.

*Leak/service test*

86 Checks on overall plant integrity following major intrusive work (for example plant overhauls) may involve various types of pressure testing to confirm that the plant is 'leak tight'. These tests will involve further temporary changes to the overall isolation scheme. A very high standard of control over the final de-isolation will be required, following the pressure test.

# Key stages of process isolation

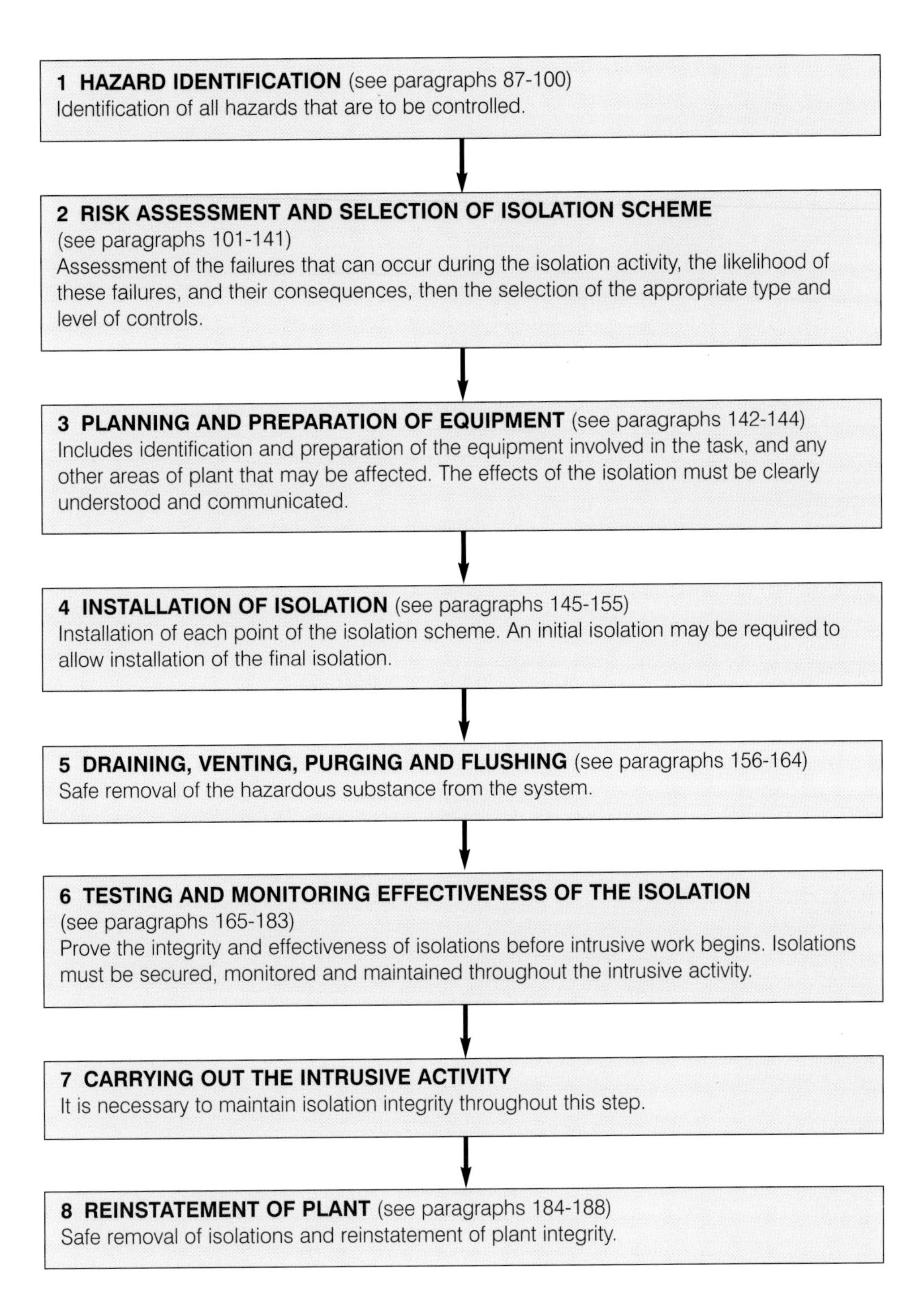


**Figure 3:** Summary of process isolation

## Hazard identification

*Hazards related to the isolated substance*
87 If isolation failure leads to loss of containment, people may be harmed. Escalation to a major accident can occur. Harm may result from a substance's flammable and toxic properties or, for example, where it:

- is present at high pressure;
- is at high or low temperatures;
- is reactive;
- can create a hazardous environment, eg leading to asphyxiation or drowning;
- can form an explosive atmosphere (including dusts); or
- remains in equipment as a sludge or hard deposit.

88 In the event of a release, the potential for a major accident will depend on a range of factors including:

- the nature and properties of the substance;
- the quantity of substance released;
- the escalation potential (ie the presence of other plant, including confining structures, and other hazardous inventories); and
- the populations at risk, their proximity to the plant and the speed with which they may be affected.

89 Release of a **flammable** substance can cause a pool, jet or flash fire, or a vapour-cloud explosion (or it may disperse without finding a source of ignition). Escalation may occur, especially in congested plant where the risks of, and consequences from, a vapour-cloud explosion are greater. The resulting overpressure may damage other plant, potentially leading to further loss of containment and additional casualties. Jet flame impingement may also critically damage adjacent plant.

90 Some **toxic** substances will have longer hazard ranges and greater potential to affect more people. They may be more persistent in the environment. If personnel exposed to a toxic substance become incapable of controlling or safely shutting down the plant, escalation could occur.

91 Storage or processing conditions can be significant. For example:

- flammable substances stored or processed at elevated temperatures may be released above their flashpoints or their auto-ignition temperatures; and
- gases at ambient temperature are often stored as liquids under pressure. Releases from pressurised storage are more energetic. For a given hole size, release rates tend to be higher.

92 The nature and scale of an incident will be determined not only by bulk inventory but also by the **rate** at which a hazardous substance is released. This influences the size of the liquid pool or flammable gas cloud formed, or the length and diameter of a jet flame.

### Reactive substances
93 Pyrophoric scale may form in hydrocarbon-processing streams where hydrogen sulphide is present. The scale can spontaneously ignite when exposed to oxygen. Necessary precautions include breaking containment in a way to minimise air currents, maintaining an inert atmosphere and/or wetting the scale. Other chemicals with the potential to spontaneously combust or react with air (eg platinised carbon catalysts) must also receive special attention.

*Hazards associated with the work task*
94 All relevant hazards should be identified, including non-process isolation hazards (Appendix 2) and personal injury hazards. Hazards should be recorded on the permit for the work task. You should consider factors such as pipe spring, insulation type and other services. Certain locations or work tasks will require additional considerations:

### Entry into confined spaces
95 Comprehensive guidance on requirements for work involving entry into confined spaces is contained in *Safe work in confined spaces*.[13] Entry into a confined space must be considered only where there is **no reasonably practicable alternative** way to carry out the work. Vessels (eg separators, tanks, reactors, distillation columns) are the most obvious form of confined space, but sumps, pig launchers or work inside pipes or machinery modules can present the same dangers.

96 The hazards from entry include:

- flammable or toxic vapours from process materials;
- toxic vapours evolved from residues or their by-products (for example carbon monoxide may be evolved when a coking vessel is first opened to atmosphere);
- asphyxiation from gases (eg nitrogen) used for inerting the confined space or adjacent areas;
- oxygen depletion;
- carbon dioxide build-up; and
- drowning by the ingress of liquid or free-flowing solid.

97 A **very high standard** of **positive** isolation should be achieved, by physical disconnection (spool removal) or the insertion of spades (**unless** use of positive isolation would not reduce risk during vessel entry – eg isolation of the safety valve on a steam boiler). Isolation points should be installed as close as possible to the vessel.

98 For certain fully welded systems (eg some high pressure steam systems/boilers), physical disconnection or spading may not be possible. In such cases, the system will normally have to be shut down to enable work which involves invasive inspection or breaching the pressure envelope.

### Hot work
99 You should eliminate or minimise hot work wherever reasonably practicable. Any proposed site weld on or near process equipment should be justified by risk assessment. Where a system contains or has contained a flammable substance, isolation to carry out hot work such as welding or grinding will require additional precautions to mitigate against risks from residual material.[14]

100 Consider the impact of hot work on any live systems in the vicinity of the worksite. You may need to isolate,

depressurise and, if appropriate, drain any systems where hot work could cause fire or inadvertently breach containment of a hazardous fluid.

## Risk assessment and selection of isolation scheme

*Risk assessment of the isolation task*

101 You should carry out intrusive work on live plant **only** if there is no reasonably practicable alternative.

102 Your procedures should specify the requirements for risk assessment of isolation and associated activities. Your assessment should include the potential for, and consequences of, human error. All relevant hazards should be considered.

103 Consider alternative ways of carrying out the overall task and identify the lowest risk option. Take into account:

- the potential consequences, in the event of isolation failure, to people, the environment and plant and equipment; and
- the likelihood of failure of each type of isolation.

104 Risk assessment should cover all stages of the isolation activity, including:

- preparatory work for the isolation – including depressurisation and release of stored energy, draining/venting, purging and washing out;
- installation/removal and proving of the isolation;
- the integrity of the isolation during intrusive work, and the compatibility of any nearby work or operations on shared systems; and
- requirements for testing and reinstatement of plant (eg pressure/leak testing, purging, controlled repressurisation/re-filling).

105 Your risk assessment should identify any need for additional mitigating measures (see paragraphs 126-127), taking into account:

- what could go wrong to lead to a loss of containment;
- the possible consequences of a loss of containment eg fire, human harm, environmental damage;
- how likely it is and how bad it could be; and
- anything else that can be done to reduce risk to ALARP levels.

106 The rigour of your risk assessment should reflect the type and severity of the hazards, and the extent to which relevant generic procedures are already in place. Adequate assessment often requires team input, including practical knowledge of both the work task and the isolation methods.

*Setting company standards*

107 You may decide to establish company isolation standards for some tasks, based on hazard and risk assessment. The range of substances, situations and tasks to which these generic standards apply – and, critically, the **limits to their application** – must be clear. Such standards should specify:

- the minimum acceptable isolation standard;
- the expected isolation method; and
- any associated risk reduction measures.

108 You should also have a system in place to ensure that, in the event of changes or enhancements to your standards, all relevant procedures will be updated.

*Selection of the final isolation method*

109 **All** isolation methods can fail (even positive isolations – particularly during installation and plant reinstatement activities). The potential for human failure is a major factor affecting the overall reliability of an isolation method. The performance of an isolation depends not only on the integrity of the isolation hardware, but also on the adequacy of the arrangements to identify each isolation point, secure the isolation, prove/monitor the isolation and maintain overall control of the work. When selecting an isolation method, you should consider the potential for both mechanical and human failure.

110 Security during the intrusive task is provided by the final isolation. An initial isolation may also be required to enable this final isolation (eg positive isolation) to be installed (see paragraphs 145-148).

111 Appendix 5 summarises a range of isolation techniques. The level of integrity provided by your selected final isolation method should match the severity of the potential hazard.

112 Your choice of final isolation method should be based on risk assessment. However, where an isolation of higher integrity is available, and where it is reasonably practicable to use it, you should do so (except where this would not reduce risk).

113 It is good practice to use **positive isolations** for confined space entries (see paragraphs 95-98), for toxic fluids and for extended isolations (see paragraphs 203-205). A key requirement during the initial isolation is to identify whether valves being used for isolation are secure and are providing a tight shut-off. Paragraphs 180-183 provide recommendations on proving valves.

114 Use physical disconnection wherever reasonably practicable – it is simpler to monitor removal of a spool than to check that a spectacle plate has been correctly installed.

**Selection tool – one means of establishing 'baseline' isolation standard**

115 Appendix 6 contains a selection tool. This is intended to **assist** in setting final isolation standards. It is based on risk assessment principles and calibrated against industry good practice for work on live plant. A selection tool can complement, **but cannot replace**, competent technical judgement and common sense. Other ways to select isolation methods may be acceptable.

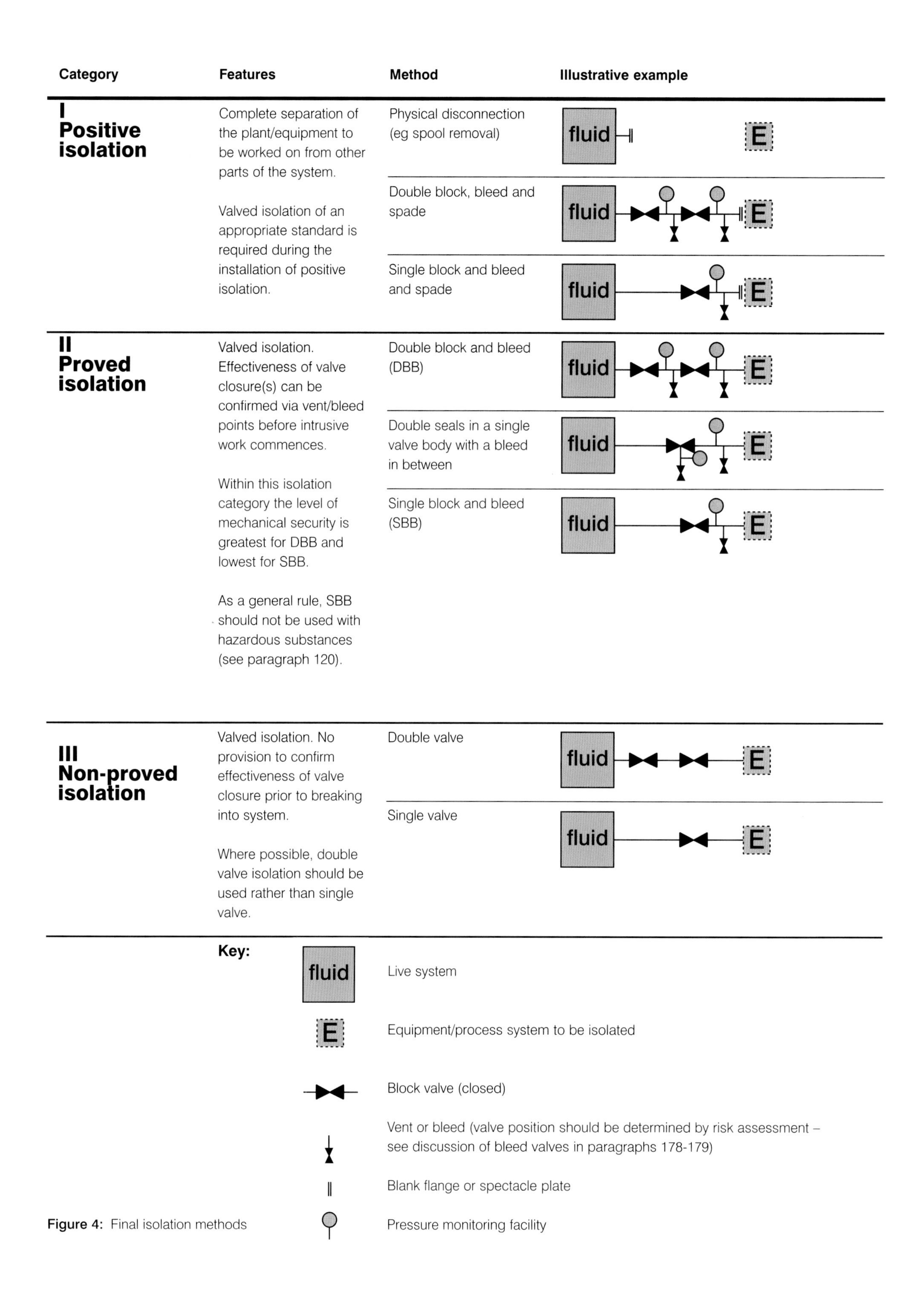

| Category | Features | Method | Illustrative example |
|---|---|---|---|
| **I Positive isolation** | Complete separation of the plant/equipment to be worked on from other parts of the system.<br><br>Valved isolation of an appropriate standard is required during the installation of positive isolation. | Physical disconnection (eg spool removal) | |
| | | Double block, bleed and spade | |
| | | Single block and bleed and spade | |
| **II Proved isolation** | Valved isolation. Effectiveness of valve closure(s) can be confirmed via vent/bleed points before intrusive work commences.<br><br>Within this isolation category the level of mechanical security is greatest for DBB and lowest for SBB.<br><br>As a general rule, SBB should not be used with hazardous substances (see paragraph 120). | Double block and bleed (DBB) | |
| | | Double seals in a single valve body with a bleed in between | |
| | | Single block and bleed (SBB) | |
| **III Non-proved isolation** | Valved isolation. No provision to confirm effectiveness of valve closure prior to breaking into system.<br><br>Where possible, double valve isolation should be used rather than single valve. | Double valve | |
| | | Single valve | |



**Figure 4:** Final isolation methods

116 The selection tool is **not** intended to apply to:

- **confined space** entries (see paragraphs 95-98);
- **pipelines** isolations (Appendix 7);
- **extended term** isolations, eg for mothballed plant (see paragraphs 203-205); or
- where isolation failure could produce a **catastrophic outcome**, or a situation from which recovery would be very difficult.

117 The tool will indicate either that further consideration is required or that one of the categories of isolation in Figure 4 is the appropriate **'baseline'** standard (note that, as discussed in Appendix 6, this may not always be the most appropriate final isolation method).

118 Within each category, the methods listed do **not** all provide an equivalent degree of security. For example, there is a hierarchy of mechanical security for the three isolation methods shown for category II (proved) isolation – once installed, the reliability of double block and bleed (DBB) is greatest while that for single block and bleed (SBB) is least.

119 Figure 4 shows an example for each isolation method. Other schemes may be equally/more appropriate. Your choice should be based on risk assessment. Remember that as the complexity of an isolation scheme increases, the opportunities for error also increase.

120 **As a general rule you should not use SBB as a final isolation method for work on live plant containing hazardous substances**, but there may be circumstances where the use of SBB is justified. SBB should be used **only** where risk assessment has shown it to be acceptable.

**Selection of 'ALARP' isolation method**

121 The flowchart at Figure 5 outlines the selection of an isolation method and risk reduction measures for an isolation scheme. The 'ideal' path is highlighted in yellow, but it is recognised that it will not always be possible to follow this route. The box shaded in grey relates to the use of 'variations' (see paragraphs 128-141).

122 After establishing your 'baseline' isolation standard, you will need to complete your risk assessment to ensure that risks are ALARP. Important aspects to consider include:

- storage conditions (eg temperature);
- additional risk reduction measures (see paragraphs 125-127);
- whether use of a 'variation' is appropriate, eg for short term isolations (see paragraphs 128-141);
- personal injury considerations, eg manual handling,[11] exposure to substances which may be hazardous to health[12] etc; and
- environmental considerations (eco-toxicity).

123 Your final considerations should be whether risk levels have been reduced to 'ALARP' and whether the level of risk associated with the proposed isolation is tolerable (see paragraph 16) – **if not, then the work should not go ahead**. No individual step should create an intolerable risk for those carrying out the work.

124 The risk associated with some proposed isolations will be such that the selection tool in Appendix 6 indicates the need for further consideration before you proceed. You may decide:

- that risk can be reduced to acceptable levels (ALARP) via risk reduction measures;
- that the isolation envelope should be extended; **or**
- that these isolations **should not** be carried out on live plant.

*Risk reduction measures*

125 Consider measures such as (but not restricted to):

- reducing pressure and/or temperature;
- reducing inventory;
- detailed planning of the work:
  - to minimise the duration of exposure to broken containment;
  - to reduce the duration of the isolation; and
  - to ensure that the correct type and quantity of PPE is immediately available;
- restricting incompatible or non-essential work nearby;
- restricting access around the worksite by barriers;
- reducing the number of people working on the plant;
- monitoring the isolation more frequently;
- having an operator in attendance throughout the isolation; and/or
- increasing supervision.

126 Contingency plans for planned isolation activities should include any necessary additional measures beyond your standard emergency arrangements for loss-of-containment incidents. You should ensure that any loss of containment can be:

- **identified rapidly** – by personnel, gas detectors, alarm and monitor systems etc;
- **stopped rapidly** – eg by identifying upstream valves for securing isolation, in particular valves which may be remotely operated;[15] and
- **contained** – eg by kerbs, bunds, temporary bunds with sandbags etc.

127 Your contingency plans should also include arrangements:

- to allow the work party to escape safely in an emergency;
- to move people away from the potential hazard (arrangements for evacuation, mustering etc); and
- to communicate necessary action to other parties – eg shutdown of adjacent plants.

*Risk assessment of variations*

128 If you cannot meet the baseline isolation standard (or your established company isolation standard, as described in paragraph 107), and it is not reasonably practicable to extend the isolation envelope or defer to shutdown, follow the pathway in the grey box in Figure 5 to establish whether you may use a 'variation' (ie whether, based on risk assessment, it is acceptable to use a lower standard of isolation).

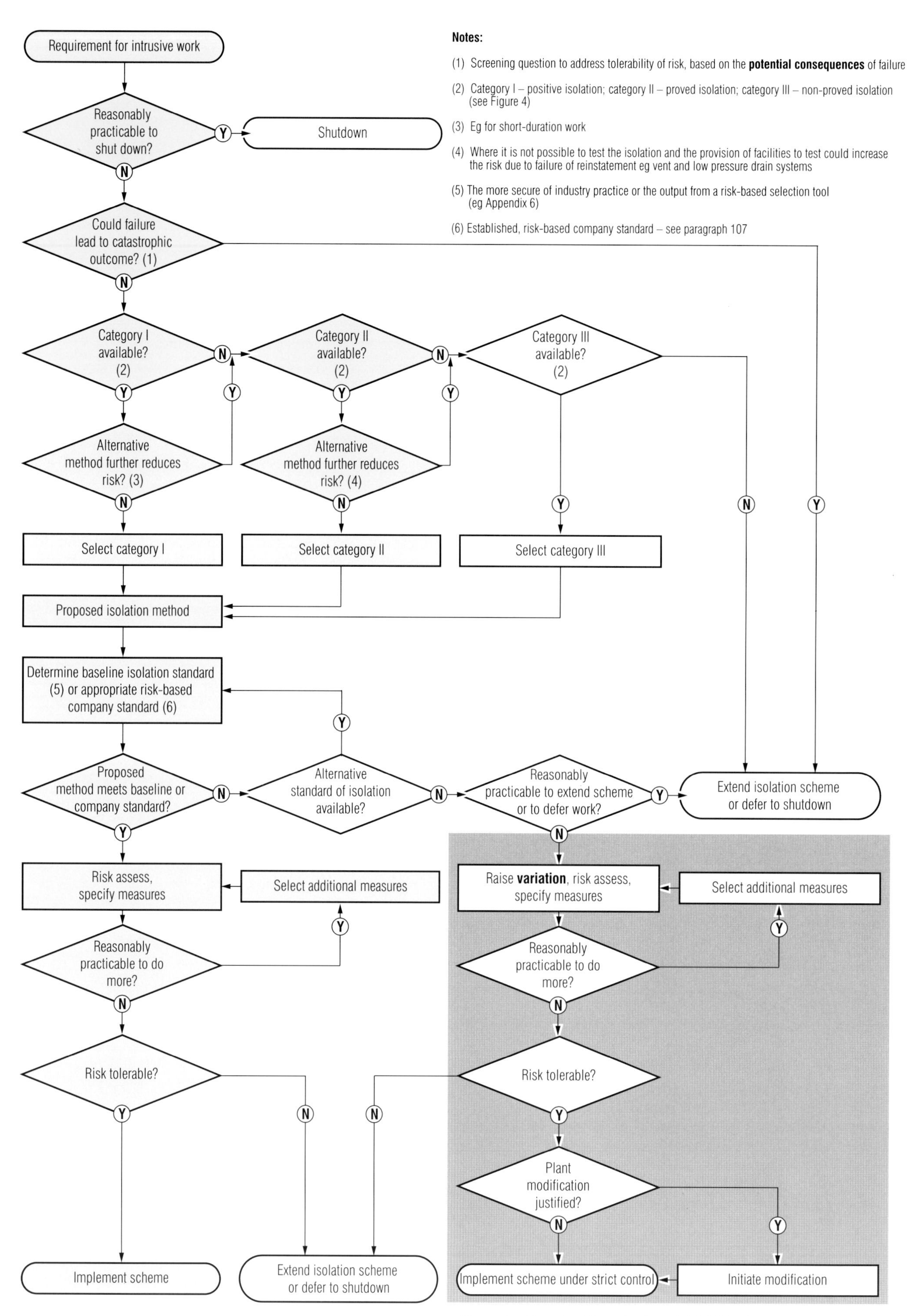


**Notes:**

(1) Screening question to address tolerability of risk, based on the **potential consequences** of failure

(2) Category I – positive isolation; category II – proved isolation; category III – non-proved isolation (see Figure 4)

(3) Eg for short-duration work

(4) Where it is not possible to test the isolation and the provision of facilities to test could increase the risk due to failure of reinstatement eg vent and low pressure drain systems

(5) The more secure of industry practice or the output from a risk-based selection tool (eg Appendix 6)

(6) Established, risk-based company standard – see paragraph 107

**Figure 5:** Flowchart for selection of ALARP isolation method

129 You should have a risk assessment and authorisation process to consider any proposed 'variations' and associated risk-reduction measures. People authorised to approve such variations should:

- be of an appropriate seniority within your organisation;
- have the technical competence to review the risk assessment (for example equivalent to the 'technical authority' who set the company standard); and
- have operational independence from those proposing the isolation scheme.

130 Use of a variation from the baseline/established company standard of isolation should be clearly indicated and explained on your documentation (eg isolation certificate) and signed by the person authorising use of the variation.

### Variations due to layout or condition of plant

131 The layout or condition of your plant may restrict your ability to safely install or use baseline isolation standards. Plant modification should be considered in these circumstances (see paragraphs 137-140).

### Variations from positive isolation requirements for short-duration work

132 The time needed to install and remove a positive isolation can be substantial. For some short-duration work this exceeds the time to carry out the intrusive work and the main loss-of-containment risk may be associated with the installation and removal of the isolation.

133 A 'variation' for short-duration work can be used only where the overall risk of undertaking the activity using positive isolation (including the risks associated with installing and removing the isolation) is greater than the overall risk if a less secure isolation method is used for the intrusive work.

134 Short-duration variations are most commonly used for the removal of instruments for repair or testing, and the changing of, for example, filter elements or control valves.

135 For work on pumps, typical short-duration tasks include:

- packing of glands;
- removal of couplings;
- replacement of mechanical seals; and
- change of lubricant.

136 For variations involving short-duration work:

- completion of the intrusive work (ie entire process from installation of isolation to recommissioning) should take less time than is needed to install and remove the final (positive) isolation;
- the work should not extend beyond one operating shift;
- the work instruction should specify the required contingency action if unforeseen difficulties cause intrusive work to overrun the single shift (reinstate the plant or install a positive isolation);
- you should prove each isolation point/valve before starting the work, and monitor for leakage during the work activity;
- the worksite should not be left unattended. This allows prompt remedial action if a leak develops; and
- mitigating action to bring any leak under control should be understood and necessary equipment available.

### Modification considerations

137 When a variation from the normal level of isolation is authorised for work on a plant, you should consider improving the isolation facilities at the first available opportunity.

138 Where plant modification will reduce risk, it should be carried out unless the costs would be grossly disproportionate to the risk reduction. Where work will be carried out on a repeated basis, this will shift the balance of risk reduction and cost towards plant modification.

139 Remember that no modification should be carried out until you have assessed the potential consequences (looking at the wider implications for the plant as a whole, not just at the specific isolation activity). Modifications should not reduce the inherent safety of the plant. For example, you should assess with great care any proposed modification to permit isolation of protective devices, where no isolation was previously permitted.

140 Previous authorisation of a variation does **not** justify its use for future interventions. Repeated use of a variation is acceptable only where your decision not to upgrade to the required standard is justified by risk assessment and risk reduction to ALARP criteria. Record the basis for such decisions. You should review the assessment each time the variation is proposed, taking into account changes on the plant and in available technology to control the residual risk.

### Monitoring the use of variations

141 The use of variations from company standards on a plant should be regularly monitored and audited. Relevant matters to scrutinise include:

**for variations:**

- the proportion of isolations carried out at lesser security than company policy;
- full compliance with a variation approval process;
- whether an alternative system of work could avoid the use of a less secure isolation method; and
- whether costs/circumstances have altered the validity of the original ALARP decision; and

**for retrofit actions:**

- that the wider implications of any proposed change are **fully** assessed prior to implementation;
- that an improvement system/plan, with a reasonable timescale, drives plant retrofit;
- that there is a phased/prioritised programme of modification; and
- how often an isolation is done at the lesser security before being remedied.

## Planning and preparation of equipment

142 Adequate planning:

- enables task-specific risk assessments to be made and actioned;
- identifies whether a larger section of the plant might need to be shut down or the work deferred;
- identifies interaction with other sections of plant subject to temporary isolation;
- involves sequencing and co-ordination of intrusive work with other plant operations;
- includes a 'walk-the-plant' step, to check that the installation matches the P&ID and, especially, that all isolation points have been identified and are accessible/ can be operated, etc;
- ensures preparation and co-ordination of job documentation such as risk assessments, method statements, permits and isolation certificates, for example by the assembly of work 'packs';
- ensures cross-referencing of relevant permits; and
- enables all necessary tools, equipment, materials, etc (including any additional personal protective equipment required for those installing and removing positive isolations) to be available at the worksite at the start of the job.

**An example**
During replacement of a heat exchanger, a vent line linking the system to a second reactor was not identified during risk assessment or during installation of the isolations. No reference had been made to P&IDs, even although the plant was congested and spread over several floors. Because of the failure to isolate the vent line, a substantial release of hydrogen bromide gas occurred when the line was opened.

*P&IDs should be used to plan isolations. Always check that they reflect the as-installed equipment. You should also walk the system to be isolated to ensure that there are no unauthorised modifications, or temporary interconnections eg by hoses.*

143 Where operation of other parts of the plant can affect the integrity of an isolation, you should prevent operation of relevant systems as part of the isolation procedure. The effect of such inhibition of plant operation should be clearly understood and communicated to **all** parties operating the plant **before** the isolation is installed.

144 Company standards should set out your arrangements for assessing, authorising and controlling overrides to safety-related systems (eg emergency shutdown systems) during isolation activities. Any such overrides, and any additional safety measures required while these systems are shut down, should be justified by risk assessment. You should not disable fire and gas detection systems and emergency shutdown systems simply to prevent spurious shutdowns. This could have wider implications. Inhibition may be appropriate, for example, where the operation of a fire-fighting system (eg use of carbon dioxide or inert gas in a confined space) during isolation/intrusive activity would put workers at risk.

## Installation of the isolation

*Stages of isolations*

145 Installation of isolations can, in practice, involve two stages:

- an initial isolation; and
- a final or full isolation.

146 The **initial isolation** is an isolation (usually valved) of relatively short duration, which enables the insertion of a positive isolation **after** the plant that is downstream of the initial isolation has been depressurised and purged. You should consider the safety of this initial isolation scheme when selecting your final isolation method.

147 The **final isolation** secures those carrying out the intrusive work, and those who might otherwise be affected, from a release of substance from the plant during the intrusive activity. Workers breaking into the system to install physical isolation will require suitable personal protective equipment to mitigate against any undetected failure of the initial isolation, or liquid or vapour trapped between the valve and the flange.

148 Use suitable blank flanges, plugs, etc to close off any open pipework. These should be appropriately rated and properly installed with the correct gaskets and securing bolts so that they can withstand the system pressure, if required, without leaking. This may include additional external mechanical restraints such as thrust blocks or 'strutting' arrangement, particularly where compression end caps are used. Flange joint bolts should be tightened in accordance with good engineering practice.[16] Devices used to seal the ends of open pipework to enable pressure testing, or specialised systems such as pipe freezing to provide local isolation, require specialised assessment. These are included in the range of isolation methods described in Appendix 5.

*Securing isolations*

149 Isolations must remain secure through the duration of the intrusive task. The **degree of security** required for an isolation will be **proportionate to the risks** resulting from isolation failure.

150 Wherever practicable, use locking arrangements or barriers to physically prevent accidental or unauthorised removal of the isolation. The need for security is greatest where a single action (for example opening a valve) could lead to the release of a hazardous fluid.

151 Some valve types are more susceptible to inadvertent opening than others. For example, ball valves (particularly those of smaller diameter) can be knocked open, especially where they are easily accessed. Always physically disable and secure (by padlocking, removal of handle etc) valves which require only a 90° movement between shut and open.

152 Figure 6 outlines a range of methods for securing isolations. More complex systems such as trapped key interlocked systems are available, as are systems that allow a number of people in a multi-disciplinary work group to apply individual locks. Your procedures should specify the systems to be used and the arrangements for administering and auditing them.

| Level of security | Methods | Typical application | Comments |
| --- | --- | --- | --- |
| Most | Locking system with secure key control<br><br>Removal of actuating mechanism | Offshore<br><br>Onshore high risk activities<br><br>Remote locations | Access to keys/actuating mechanism controlled separately to work party, eg by a *lockout box* |
| | Locking system, eg chains or cables to secure valve, with tagging reference to permit<br><br>Handwheel covers | All locations | Work party has access to keys<br><br>Effort by others to defeat the barrier depends on the material (a plastic tie can be more easily cut through than a metal chain) |
| Least | Tagging only | Where there is tight control of the isolation point/work area and lower process hazards | No security – procedural control only<br><br>Requires constant attendance of the work party<br><br>No control of the isolation independent to the work party – may be appropriate for certain 'own isolation' tasks |

**Figure 6:** Examples of methods for securing isolations

153 Where a remotely actuated valve is part of an isolation scheme, you should prevent inadvertent valve operation on command. Appropriate measures to ensure this should be specified by a competent person:

- the valve should first be closed;
- where motive power (electricity, air or hydraulic fluid) is required for closure, the valve must be mechanically constrained from opening by an appropriate locking system, and the isolation tested after de-energising the motive power supply/supplies;
- where absence of motive power is required for valve closure, the isolation must be tested after de-energising the motive power supply;
- in both cases the motive power supply should be isolated by physical disconnection. Unauthorised de-isolation should be prevented by work permit controls. Motive power disconnection points should be labelled and described with their status recorded and maintained on an isolation certificate, or similar document, as part of the work permit control. This is particularly important for suitable reinstatement of the equipment;
- where isolation of motive power is effected by venting, the vent valves should be secured in the open position by a locking arrangement selected in proportion to the risk;
- where electrical power is switched off and the fuse removed, the means of isolation must be secured by locking off (see Appendix 2). Keys and locks used to secure the isolation must be issued in accordance with work permit control;
- methods for securing isolation of motive power should be selected in proportion to the risk;
- where remotely actuated valves are controlled by third parties, a suitable protocol for communication and work permit control must be developed; and
- special consideration should be given to reinstatement of remotely actuated valves located an appreciable distance away from the worksite.

154 All plant and equipment relating to an isolation should be clearly identified on the worksite. You should consider permanent labelling for this purpose. All isolation points, including bleeds and spades, should be fully documented and referenced within the work control system to ensure the correct position and sequencing of all the components associated with an isolation scheme (eg the position of vents, the removal of physical isolations). This is in addition to full checks at the worksite.

155 Attach an isolation tag to each component of an isolation scheme, including bleeds and spades. This checks that all necessary isolations are in place and gives a visual indication that a device is in active use as a means of isolation. Tag numbers should match the line diagrams in the isolation documentation.

## Draining, venting, purging and flushing (DVPF)

156 Where systems contain hazardous substances, remove the bulk contents and, as necessary, cool and clean away residual fluids and any solid deposits before breaking containment. Bleeds or vents are pipework connections that allow fluid to be drained or depressurised from the system. They enable safe depressurisation of parts of the plant and are necessary to check the integrity of isolations. Inadequate provision and siting of bleeds or vents may compromise the safety of an isolation.

157 Venting and draining will be required prior to installation and testing of an isolation where:

- a positive isolation is installed/removed. This intrusive work will require prior valved isolation, venting and draining; or
- the isolation method, eg double block and bleed (DBB), requires removal of the fluid to prove integrity of the isolation.

158 Hazardous substances should be removed without:

- overloading the drains and/or vent systems;
- inadvertent/uncontrolled ingress of air into pipework and equipment;
- formation of ice/hydrates; or
- creating a vacuum in vessels not designed for the purpose.

159 Information on the hardware and safe systems of work for draining, venting, purging and flushing (DVPF) is included in Appendix 8.

160 Your work control documents should record:

- the hazards related to carrying out DVPF and the necessary risk-reduction controls;
- the level of isolation necessary to allow DVPF activities; and
- the required level of cleanliness and how to show/test that this has been reached.

161 The necessary extent of purging and flushing will depend on the substance concerned and the nature of the intrusive activity. For example, very stringent control is required where intrusive hot work is to be carried out on systems that have contained flammable substances.[10] Precautions may include:

- depressurise to atmospheric pressure;
- cool (or heat, for cryogenic systems);
- drain;
- water flush and/or fill;
- nitrogen purge;
- others such as air movement, high-pressure water jetting, back flushing, detergent wash; and
- demonstrating a non-explosive atmosphere (substantially below lower explosive limit (LEL)), internally, immediately before the work starts.

162 Specify arrangements for control, calibration and checking of test equipment in your procedures. Where necessary, ensure that gas testing equipment is suitable for use after purging (ie that measurements will not be adversely affected by the presence of inert gas or depleted levels of oxygen).

163 When testing plant and pipelines to prove that they are totally gas or vapour-free, ensure that a representative sample is taken. For large items of plant, you may need top, middle and bottom samples to ensure that no light or heavy gases remain.

164 Testing of pipelines requires special care, as the point of isolation may be some distance from the sampling point. In such circumstances you should consider installing a sample point closer to the isolation point to verify its gas or vapour-free status.

## Testing and monitoring effectiveness of the isolation

165 Prove the integrity of **all** isolation points of an isolation scheme **before** proceeding with intrusive work (unless your risk assessment has indicated that use of non-proved isolation is acceptable):

- each part of the isolation should be proved separately, eg prove each valve in a double block and bleed scheme;
- each part should be proved to the highest pressure which can be expected within the system during the work activity. Particular care is required when there is a low differential pressure across valves where the sealing mechanism is activated by pressure; and
- where possible, each part of the isolation should be proved in the direction of the expected pressure differential.

166 For a **positive isolation scheme**, there are two stages of testing. Prove both the initial (valved) isolation and the final isolation.

167 Your procedure for installing the isolation should clearly specify the arrangements for proving the isolation, the test success criteria and, for positive isolations, the pressure to be applied (see paragraphs 180-183).

168 Do not rely on an isolation that is unproved because the facilities are not present, or where you lack confidence in the test. Extend the isolation boundary or defer the work until shutdown. You should also consider plant modification to install facilities for testing that isolation point in future (see paragraphs 138-139).

169 The flowchart at Figure 7 steps through the process of testing and outlines next actions if the isolation point fails the test.

170 Fluids which have the potential to foul or plug small-bore pipework can lead to false results (for example the use of drain valves to verify depressurisation may give a false result due to blockages in the drain line). You may need to flush small-bore pipework to prove that it is clear. Clearance of blockages is a specialist area and should be attempted only by those who have sufficient expertise.

171 Isolation and proving can be made more difficult by:

- viscous fluids, particularly if they solidify at temperatures near ambient;
- 'dirty' services where debris, residues, scale, etc may have settled into drain lines or into valves, preventing seating; and

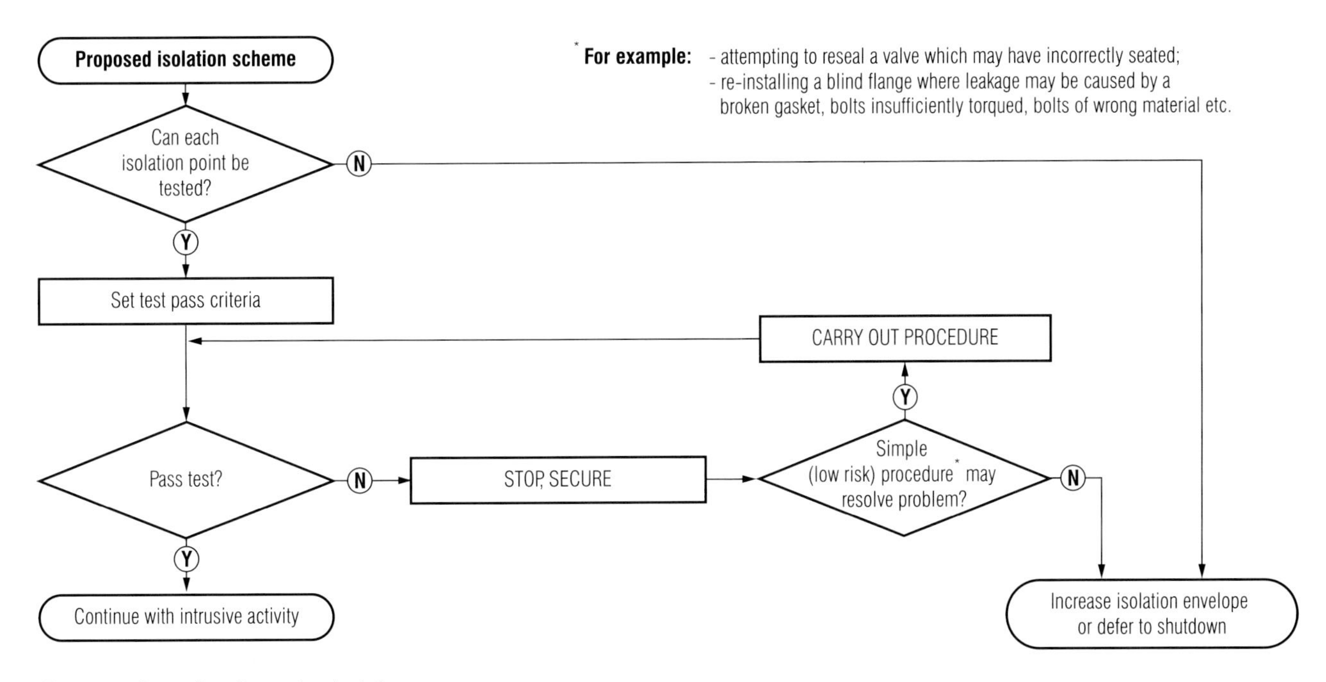


**Figure 7:** Procedure for testing isolations

- hydrates (certain mixtures of hydrocarbons and water). These can form an ice-like solid at certain pressures and temperatures, blocking valves and pipework. Pressure tests may then give misleading results. Subsequent melting of the hydrates can lead to release of any trapped pressure.

172 Care is needed when you use pressure gauges to confirm the absence of pressure or leaks.

**Pressure gauges**

When using pressure gauges while depressurising plant, consider the following points:

- pressure gauges are reliable indicators of the existence of pressure but not of complete depressurisation. Check an open vent or needle valve for final confirmation of zero pressure before breaking into the system;
- pressure gauges normally give accurate indications only over the middle part of their range and gauges designed to measure high pressures often give poor pressure response at low pressures. If you use pressure gauges to monitor plant blowdown or to check isolation integrity, two gauges with different ranges may be necessary – the procedures should protect a low pressure range gauge; and
- you should prove pressure gauges before use by testing against a pressure source.

173 Immediately prior to breaking containment, a competent person should prove that there is no leakage and pressure build-up within the isolation envelope, using an appropriate method. This should be recorded on the isolation certificate to demonstrate the test results to those undertaking the work.

### Monitoring

174 You should monitor the integrity of isolations during the work period. Re-prove isolations that will remain in place for longer than one shift or which have been left unattended. Determine the frequency of monitoring and re-proving by risk assessment, and specify this frequency within your procedures.

175 Use bleeds or vents to confirm that there is no leakage past the isolation, by periodically checking for any pressure build-up in the space between the elements of the isolation. For hazardous process fluids, ensure that you route vents and drains to a safe place or safely contain any leakage.

176 Pressure gauges should be fitted where a cavity is bled/vented and may also be needed in other situations. They should have a suitable range and sensitivity to detect pressure build-up.

177 Where a blank flange is to be used but the plant has no appropriate vent to enable the safe release of any pressure build-up, you should consider using a blank flange in which a suitable vent is incorporated.

### Position of bleed valves etc

178 Your risk assessment will identify the appropriate position for bleed valves during intrusive work. Relevant factors include:

- the inherent hazard of the fluid;
- the fluid state;
- the type of collection or disposal system available;
- the location of any open end of the bleed or vent in relation to the worksite;
- the ability to detect any leakage; and
- the level of confidence that the isolation valves are not leaking and can withstand overpressures which may develop from other parts of the system.

179 Unless risk assessment indicates an alternative to be safer, bleed valves connected to a downstream closed live header or drainage system should remain secured in the **closed** position throughout an isolation, so that:

- the isolated space cannot be pressurised should the disposal system become pressurised due to other operations/incidents; and
- any leakage through the isolation valves into the space downstream of valves can be monitored directly at the cavity. You should then re-close the valves and re-establish the bleed position.

**Proving the isolation**

180 Isolation valves do not always provide a leak-tight seal. In such cases, for isolation integrity to be proved, the isolation point must not let past more than a specified quantity of fluid over a defined period of time. You should define these criteria within your procedures. The acceptable 'passing' criteria and period of time will depend on the substance concerned and the piping volume available to relieve pressure build-up.

181 Any decision to carry out intrusive work with a known leakage rate is acceptable **only** if it is based upon a specific risk assessment that demonstrates the residual risk to be tolerable. Your assessment should include the following issues, where relevant. These should be satisfied before work starts:

- the leakage does not impinge on the worksite, or cause additional hazard to either personnel or plant;
- the leakage can be safely disposed of away from the worksite. Depending on the nature and hazard of the fluid (and on which element of a double valve isolation is leaking), this may include:
  - providing adequate catchment under the open pipe end;
  - fitting a blank capable of retaining full system pressure with venting/bleeding facilities to the open pipe end;
  - ensuring that any interconnecting space (for example between two valves) is vented and drained at appropriate intervals to avoid pressurisation, taking into account risks associated with repeatedly draining the fluid; or
  - special arrangements such as establishing a continuous purge;
- the leakage rate can be monitored – where an isolation valve shows a small degree of leakage, over time this leakage is likely to increase. It may be appropriate to appoint a person to stand by, who has the authority to stop the work if the leakage rate exceeds pre-determined acceptable levels, and who is independent of the work party;
- you have a contingency plan to make the equipment safe (eg by upstream isolation or remote shutdown of the plant) in the event of a sudden and/or significant increase in leakage rate; and
- the maintenance team are aware of the potential for sudden release of system fluid and the necessary emergency actions.

182 Where an entire isolation is passing (ie a single valve isolation which cannot be shown to be leak tight, or a double valve isolation in which both valves are passing), its use should be proposed only in exceptional circumstances. This is likely to be justifiable only for non-hazardous fluids (for example during repairs on a firewater pump where an isolation valve passes water into a non-confined worksite, it might be better to continue rather than to isolate a portion of the firewater mains system, so reducing firefighting capability).

183 If testing fails to confirm a satisfactory isolation, reinstate the isolation points to a safe condition, secure them and reassess the situation. You may need to shut down a larger section of plant to achieve a satisfactory isolation.

## Reinstatement of the plant

184 Recommissioning requires equivalent controls to those used during installation of isolation. Where work has been controlled under multiple permits, dependent on common isolation points, it is critical to define the sequence of plant reinstatement.

185 Controls should include a check of all cross-referenced permits in force and their related isolations (including instrumentation isolations), to confirm the safety of other work following plant reinstatement. Ensure that any plant control and protection systems functions that were overridden for the purposes of the isolations are restored to their normal condition.

186 Take care when removing a positive isolation. Hazardous substances can build up behind the blank or spade if a valve leaks. Always check vents or drains before the spade or blank is removed. If you detect a leak behind the isolation, resecure the vent or drain and stop work until a safe system for the removal is in place.

187 Use appropriate documentation, such as isolation certificates, to log all disturbed items on a plant and to control their reinstatement. Reinstatement and recommissioning of plant must be properly planned, to include:

- confirmation of plant integrity before removing isolations; and
- identifying the effects of removing the isolation and restarting plant on other isolations and systems.

188 Systems and procedures that assure the full reinstatement of plant and the integrity of the process area include:

- control of all disturbed joints;[16]
- blank/blind register to control removal of blank/blinds for isolation, purging, flushing, pressure testing etc;
- purging procedures and records;
- quality assurance controls on maintenance hand back of intrusive activities during shutdown;
- full visual system check by operations personnel against the system P&ID and check that no isolation tags remain on the plant;
- system service testing and leak testing records and procedures;
- full visual valve position (open, shut, locked, free) check against plan for start up; and
- additional monitoring after recommissioning.

# Isolation situations requiring specific considerations

## Own isolations

189 The **separation** of isolation activity and intrusive work is usually assured by PTW arrangements. However, for 'own isolations' the **same person** makes the isolations **and** performs the intrusive work.

190 Such arrangements are generally appropriate only for prescribed categories of work of limited risk and release potential. Typically, this applies to repetitive tasks of very short duration work.

191 Own isolations normally fall into the following types:

- routine plant operator activities, for example:
  - removing, cleaning and reinstating filters from pressure envelopes;
  - process sampling;
- **third party maintenance** of specialist vendor kit; and
- isolation of **instrument systems** for maintenance where these are designed to be isolated from process plant streams (Appendix 9). Typically this might include transmitters, impulse lines, sight-glasses, analytical instruments and gauges.

**An example**
Production operators were carrying out maintenance on a filter. The pump serving the filter was isolated only via software – and a demand signal from the plant overrode the pump de-selection. A ball valve between the pump and the filter was closed, but may have been passing. A joint in the plastic pipeline failed. The operators were sprayed with sodium hypochlorite.

*All equipment within the isolation boundary should be de-energised so that control signals do not affect the integrity of the isolation. The isolating valve should be tested and secured. Disconnections of motive power should be recorded and checked-off during reinstatement.*

192 You should identify by risk assessment whether procedural or PTW control is appropriate for own isolations.

193 Where own isolations are carried out under procedural control, standardisation of equipment (plant design) is particularly important.

194 Where the consequences of error in applying the procedural controls could be safety critical, activities should be controlled by PTW. Work which affects process control and/or safety systems (eg involves removal of process indication, control, alarm or trip functions) should **always** be carried out under PTW. Work control by procedure is also inappropriate where a task cannot be fully defined. Remember that no person should issue a permit for their own activity.[10]

195 Own isolations require that:

- isolation, intrusive work and reinstatement are carried out by the same person;
- that person is competent to perform the isolation, to undertake the task and to reinstate the equipment;
- the isolation is under the control of the competent person, who is continuously present at the worksite while the pressure envelope is breached;
- the isolation points are identified and secured unless they are all within sight/reach of the 'own-isolator' (who must then remain in attendance for the duration of the work); and
- communication with any appropriate control room or operating unit (eg by radio) is available throughout the task.

196 In addition, for own isolations performed by competent instrument technicians:

- the permit-to-work will identify any potential residual risks and specify the appropriate control measures, including mitigation measures in case of loss of containment;
- relevant control room operators should be involved in PTW authorisation for work on systems which impact on safe control of the plant eg instrumented safety-related functions and many process control functions; and
- independent checking of reinstatement is necessary where failure to reopen an isolation valve after completion of instrument work might defeat a safety- related function, and this may not be self-revealing.

**An example**
During preventative maintenance an instrument technician carried out some local isolations to remove a number of pressure gauges. He took these to the instrument workshop. Approximately one hour later an operator noticed a smell of gas. This could have been due to leakage past a closed valve or a blockage in the pipework that subsequently cleared. The instrument technician had failed to cap the open end of the pipework.

*Own isolations should always be conducted in accordance with site-specific operating instructions or procedures. Short-term isolations using a single valve should be attended at all times, and contingency measures identified in the event of a release of process fluids.*

## Arrangements for large-scale isolations

197 Special arrangements for the isolation of a plant or section of plant may be used for intrusive work when that plant is shut down. Security of plant isolation from adjacent 'live' systems should equal, or exceed, the normal site isolation standards.

198 **'Boundary isolation'** is the insertion of fully pressure rated spades or spectacle blinds at every point of the plant boundary (the 'battery limits'). Typically, such isolation is used on plant maintenance shutdowns or 'turnarounds' where the inventory of hazardous fluids is removed. Full physical isolation of the boundary prevents re-pressurisation of the system by, or ingress of hazardous materials from, any adjacent live process systems.

199 After boundary isolation and inventory removal, arrangements for equipment isolation (for each intrusive activity) will include:

- installing a local isolation, to ensure full separation from any residual hazardous material that may be trapped within the plant; and
- local de-inventory and gas test.

200 In practice, the geographical area of a boundary isolation may contain live pipework (eg utility systems which feed adjacent plant). You should ensure that those working in the area are **fully aware** of the presence and live status of such systems.

201 A staged installation of the boundary isolation can allow fluids to be processed out (for example, flare headers are normally the last system to be isolated as they are the primary route for de-inventorying and gas freeing the plant). Until the full boundary isolation is in place, you should control any intrusive work on an item of equipment under normal site isolation procedures and a fully pressure rated spade or an equivalent level of isolation should be inserted on that equipment.

202 Additional isolation and de-isolation activity within the shutdown boundary will be needed where temporary connections into systems are required for nitrogen purging, pressure testing, etc. Rigorous arrangements are necessary to assure full reinstatement of all disturbed elements of plant. The integrity of systems within the boundary isolations should be proved prior to removal of the boundary isolation.

## Extended isolations

203 A clear record should be kept of any isolations which are to remain on the plant after work is complete. Such isolation should be the subject of formal risk assessment and change control.

204 'Extended term' isolations (eg parts of plant which have been mothballed) should be marked on the plant P&IDs. These should be positively isolated. Appropriate controls include:

- a register which identifies all such isolations and the reasons for isolation;
- a system to periodically check the status and integrity of each isolation; and
- periodic review of the status of each item to decide if the isolation is still appropriate, whether the equipment should be permanently removed etc.

205 You should also consider the need for additional measures such as nitrogen purging.

# Appendix 1: Legal requirements

## Universal application

*Health and Safety at Work etc Act 1974 Ch37* The Stationery Office 1974 ISBN 0 10 543774 3

*Management of Health and Safety at Work Regulations 1999* SI 1999/3242 The Stationery Office 1999 ISBN 0 11 085625 2

*Provision and Use of Work Equipment Regulations 1998* SI 1998/2306 The Stationery Office 1998 ISBN 0 11 079599 7

*Control of Substances Hazardous to Health Regulations 2002* SI 2002/2677 The Stationery Office 2002 ISBN 0 11 042919 2

*Dangerous Substances and Explosive Atmospheres Regulations 2002* SI 2002/2776 The Stationery Office 2002 ISBN 0 11 042957 5 (only partial application offshore)

*Personal Protective Equipment at Work Regulations 1992* SI 1992/2966 The Stationery Office 1992 ISBN 0 11 025832 0

*Manual Handling Operations Regulations 1992* SI 1992/2793 The Stationery Office 1992 ISBN 0 11 025920 3

*Lifting Operations and Lifting Equipment Regulations 1998* SI 1998/2307 The Stationery Office 1998 ISBN 0 11 079598 9

## Offshore

*Offshore Installations (Prevention of Fire and Explosion, and Emergency Response) Regulations 1995* SI 1995/743 The Stationery Office 1995 ISBN 0 11 052751 8

*Offshore Installations (Safety Case) Regulations 1992* SI 1992/2885 The Stationery Office 1992 ISBN 0 11 025869 X

*Offshore Installations and Wells (Design and Construction) Regulations 1996* SI 1996/913 The Stationery Office 1996 ISBN 0 11 054451 X

*Offshore Installations and Pipeline Works (Management and Administration) Regulations 1995* SI 1995/738 The Stationery Office 1995 ISBN 0 11 052735 6

*Offshore Installations (Safety Representatives and Safety Committees) Regulations 1989* SI 1989/971 The Stationery Office 1989 ISBN 0 11 096971 5

## Onshore

*Pressure Systems Safety Regulations 2000* SI 2000/128 The Stationery Office 2000 ISBN 0 11 085836 0

*Confined Spaces Regulations 1997* SI 1997/1713 The Stationery Office 1997 ISBN 0 11 064643 6

*Workplace (Health, Safety and Welfare) Regulations 1992* SI 1992/3004 The Stationery Office 1992 ISBN 0 11 025804 5

*Safety Representatives and Safety Committees Regulations 1977* SI 1977/500 The Stationery Office 1997 ISBN 0 11 070500 9

*Health and Safety (Consultation with Employees) Regulations 1996* SI 1996/1513 The Stationery Office 1996 ISBN 0 11 054839 6

## Onshore major hazards

*Control of Major Accident Hazards Regulations 1999* SI 1999/743 The Stationery Office 1999 ISBN 0 11 082192 0

## Pipelines

*Pipelines Safety Regulations 1996* SI 1996/825 The Stationery Office 1996 ISBN 0 11 054373 4

# Appendix 2: Non-process isolation hazards

1 Any inadvertent movement of machinery or sudden release of potential energy in mechanical, electrical or pressure form is a hazard to workers. Requirements for isolation from sources of energy to enable maintenance to be carried out safely are contained in the guidance to the *Provision and Use of Work Equipment Regulations 1998*.[6]

2 You should ensure co-ordination and sequencing of all the necessary forms of isolations (eg the electrical isolation of equipment is closely linked with its process/mechanical isolations).

## Hazards associated with mechanical machinery

3 Guidance in this section is intended for application to process machinery (not to other machinery such as powered access equipment).

4 Isolate hydraulic, pneumatic and process powered machinery by closing the appropriate isolation valves. Prevent any possibility of machinery movement by disconnecting the power fluid supply and return pipes, or otherwise making safe.

5 Isolate engine-driven machinery by shutting off the engine fuel supply and then isolating all the starting systems. For electrically driven machinery, switch off the power supply to the motor and ensure that the equipment is securely disconnected and separated from all sources of electrical energy.

6 Any residual mechanical, electrical or pressure energy which may be locked within any part of the machinery mechanism should be safely released as follows:

- **mechanical** – high and low speed rotating elements need to be run down and springs released;
- **electrical** – capacitors should be discharged and batteries disconnected and/or removed;
- **hydraulic** – accumulators and pressurised pipework should be depressurised;
- **pneumatic** – the system should be depressurised. If valves could be operated by residual trapped air, the line should also be disconnected;
- **services** – steam, gas or fuel may need to be depressurised, vented, purged or drained.

7 Even after disconnection of machinery power systems, or prevention of engines/motors from starting, there may still be a risk for people working on the machinery if it were to move (eg due to gravity). If so, fit a device such as a properly engineered *chock* or a *scotch* to lock the machinery in a safe position.

## Hazards associated with electrical equipment

8 Hazards to workers include electric shock, electrical burns, and electrical arcing resulting in the ignition of flammable gas, vapours or materials. The provision of a safe system of work is fundamental to the effective control of risks. Guidance on the isolation of high voltage electrical equipment (ie above 1000V ac or 1500V dc) is excluded from the scope of this document, only low voltage equipment is considered. Further guidance on these matters, and on effecting and securing electrical isolations is available in the *Memorandum of guidance on the Electricity at Work Regulations 1989*,[17] and *Electricity at work: Safe working practices*.[18]

9 The main power circuit of the electrical equipment, plus any associated auxiliary circuits which constitute a hazard, should be electrically isolated. Disconnect and separate the electrical equipment from **every** source of electrical energy. Discharge any stored energy in the electrical circuits, taking particular care with batteries and capacitors.

10 Devices suitable for isolation include (see BS EN 60947 series of standards[19]):

- circuit breakers with the required contact separation and locking facilities;
- disconnectors (commonly referred to as *isolators*) with locking facilities;
- switch disconnectors with locking facilities;
- plug and socket outlets;
- fuse links; and
- removable links.

11 You are advised to verify that all switching devices used for electrical isolation provide adequate contact separation, as some older devices do not provide proper separation.

12 You are strongly advised **not** to use miniature circuit breakers (MCB) as disconnectors because confirming a positive contact separation is generally not possible. In such cases, you should take alternative and/or extra measures to establish a positive air gap, eg disconnecting the circuit conductors, but only **after** you have proved them to be dead.

13 The opening of switches in the control circuits for circuit breakers, contactors and other electro-mechanical devices is **not** adequate to achieve electrical isolation. You should **not** use semiconductor devices as a means of electrical isolation.

14 Secure the means of electrical isolation by locking in the 'off' position. Your control procedures should ensure that fuses or links that have been removed are held secure. Some designs of fuse carrier allow for the use of an insulated insert, which may be lockable, to prevent unauthorised replacement of the fuse.

## Radioactive sources

15 Radioactive sources are used for inspection and measurement purposes in various instruments. The source can normally be withdrawn into a shroud or housing in the instruments and this should be confirmed prior to carrying out nearby work by checking radiation dose rates. For extensive work, it may be necessary to remove the device to a secure source store to prevent it being damaged. See *Ionising Radiations Regulations 1999 – Approved Code of Practice and guidance*.[20]

16 Some onshore and offshore process plant and piping may contain low specific activity (LSA) scale. Build-up of scale can give rise to significant external radiation and if allowed to dry out, may pose a risk of release and inhalation during intrusive work on that equipment.

## Static electricity

17 Vessel cleaning using high pressure water, solvent or steam jetting can create static electricity hazards. Guidance and advice on controlling the generation of electrostatic charges arising from jetting and other activities is contained in the British Standard *Electrostatics, Code of Practice for the avoidance of hazards due to static electricity*.[21]

# Appendix 3: Checklists for monitoring and review

## Compliance monitoring checklist – do we do what we say we do?

- The model list below should be tailored to suit your own isolation systems. It should **not** be assumed to be a comprehensive model.
- Forms should allow the checker to assign relative importance of non-conformances, record the passing of the findings up the management chain to agree/implement actions, etc.

| Isolation scheme examined: Status (live, complete):<br>Date: Checker: | Y, N, N/A | Actions, comments |
|---|---|---|
| **Systems/procedures** | | |
| 1 Is purpose of isolation stated in documentation? | | |
| 2 Is the isolation scheme correctly supported:<br>(a) by a permit-to-work? (Is cross-referenced documentation present/correct?); or<br>(b) by operational procedure (attached/available?); or<br>(c) within defined exceptional 'own-isolation' work? | | |
| 3 If work requires isolation certificate, is certificate in place and correctly completed? | | |
| 4 **For every isolation point**, does isolation method comply with/exceed company standard? | | |
| 5 If not, has variation been assessed/authorised? | | |
| 6 Have additional controls (both risk reduction and mitigation) required by assessment been identified in isolation documentation? | | |
| 7 Have testing and proving requirements/frequency been defined? | | |
| 8 **For completed isolation**, has paperwork been closed out for full reinstatement of plant? | | |
| **People** | | |
| 9 Have all people involved in planning, approving and carrying out this isolation been authorised as competent to do so? | | |
| 10 Are other affected people (eg operators of adjacent plant) aware of status of isolated equipment? | | |
| **Worksite** | | |
| 11 Are all isolation points identified on the plant and do they match the line diagram and isolation certificate? | | |
| 12 Does the installation exactly match the line diagram mark-up and isolation certificate? | | |
| 13 Has safe access been provided to all isolation points? | | |
| 14 Are all precautions specified in the permit/procedure in place? | | |
| 15 Is every point of the plant/equipment isolated? | | |
| 16 Are all bleeds and vent valves in the correct position? | | |
| 17 Are the valves immobilised? | | |
| 18 Are pressure rating and construction material marked on relevant line blinds, blank flanges, etc? | | |
| 19 Has security of isolation been demonstrated to checker? | | |
| 20 For isolation in place for longer than one shift, is there ongoing monitoring of the security of the isolation? | | |
| 21 **For completed isolation**, has all equipment been fully reinstated and have all control/safety functions been restored? | | |

## Checklist for company review of adequacy of SMS for isolations

- This checklist provides a basis (structured around the HSG653 model) for reviewing the adequacy of your safety management system (SMS) for isolation activities. Select the questions appropriate to your site and its hazards. You should also assess whether any additional questions will be appropriate for your operation.

**1 POLICY**

...states the objectives of the isolations system and a commitment to continuous improvement, eg *to reduce the risk of release of a hazardous substance to ALARP*.

1 Are policy objectives set for isolation systems, which include commitment to ALARP risk reduction and to continuous improvement?

2 Where appropriate, is focus on major accident hazards emphasised?

**2 ORGANISING**

**Control:** roles and responsibilities for isolation system are allocated and performance standards are set.

3 Are responsibilities allocated for all roles related to isolations, including:

(a) 'High level' assessment of site operations which require isolation, especially where the consequences of failure may result in a major accident?

(b) Drawing up site standards and procedures for isolations based on results of 'high level' assessment?

(c) Implementation and oversight of the overall isolation system on site?

(d) Setting performance standards?

(e) Training/competence of all relevant personnel?

(f) Planning activities in support of isolations, including site survey, carrying out 'task' risk assessments and preparing work documents (eg isolation certificates, P&IDs)?

(g) Installing and removing isolations?

(h) Permissioning isolation scheme proposals that do not comply with site standards?

(i) Proving and monitoring the security of isolations?

(j) Monitoring, audit and review of isolations systems?

4 Are individuals appointed/authorised for key roles on site (eg to issue isolation certificates, to make isolations)?

**2 ORGANISING**

**Co-operation:** between all parties involved in isolations work.

5 Do arrangements enable co-operation between production and maintenance staff, duty holder and contractors and with adjacent plant?

6 Are there mechanisms for workforce consultation and participation in isolations issues, through safety committees, workshops, workforce suggestion schemes, toolbox talks, etc?

**2 ORGANISING**

**Communication:** formal and thorough between all parties involved in isolations work.

7 Do communication methods on site cover key stages of work, for example:

(a) Pre-work meetings with all involved personnel?

(b) Work stages of shift handover, reinstatement of work?

8 Is factual information unambiguous, for example to:

(a) Identify, and communicate to operators the status of plant/equipment which is subject to isolation?

(b) Uniquely identify and tag all isolation points on the plant?

**2 ORGANISING**

**Competence:** appropriate levels developed and maintained for managers, employees and contractors involved in isolations systems.

9 Is there a system to develop and maintain the required competencies for isolations work that covers:

(a) Identification of training needs for managers, supervisors, risk assessors, supervisors, employees, contractors?

(b) Verification of training?

(c) Keeping a record on site of competent and authorised persons?

(d) Performance standards for training?

10 Do people appointed to isolations work show understanding of the types of isolations that are made on site, the way that these can go wrong and how they can mitigate the consequences of those failures?

### 3 PLANNING AND IMPLEMENTING

Risk assessment underpins the isolations systems and effective procedures enable implementation of control measures.

11 Have site standards and procedures been implemented, based on a 'high level' assessment of risk?
12 Are resources (people, time, equipment, funding) available to implement isolations systems?
13 Are the arrangements for isolations comprehensive, including isolations required in the course of routine (planned) maintenance, non-routine (breakdown) maintenance, operational activities (eg sampling), extended isolations?
14 Do arrangements cover all workers, including contractors and their employees?
15 Is there a process to consider isolation facilities (inherently safer design) for new plant, modified plant and significant changes?
16 Is there a procedure for selection of a minimum isolation method and a process to confirm that the overall arrangement is ALARP or to prohibit a proposed isolation scheme of intolerable risk?
17 Is there a variation process to permission any variation from the site standards?
18 Does a plant modification process drive proposed improvements to isolation facilities identified in the course of approving variations?
19 Is the need to isolate minimised, eg carrying out intrusive maintenance during shutdowns where possible?
20 Are conditions specified for the use of standard isolation schemes and are they periodically reviewed?
21 Is there a clear interface between work control systems (eg permit-to-work, work instructions) and isolations arrangements?
22 Does the overall task risk assessment take account of all related plant and work associated with the isolation requirements?
23 Does the task risk assessment include mitigatory measures, if the isolation fails?
24 Is there a process to review isolation aspects of a task if the job scope changes?
25 Are there arrangements to assure safe venting and draining of hazardous fluids?
26 Are the requirements to prove/monitor isolations recorded in the job documentation?
27 Are there arrangements to assure removal of isolations and reinstatement of plant, which includes operational personnel standing by for fitting and removal of physical isolations?
28 Are P&IDs available and kept updated for all areas of the plant?
29 Is there a 'walk-the-plant' check against the P&IDs to check that the correct isolations have been specified and are in place?
30 Are all isolation valves required to be secured in position to prevent them from being opened?

### 4 MEASURING PERFORMANCE

Active and reactive monitoring of the performance of isolations systems.

31 Are performance standards for isolations systems set and monitored?
32 Does active monitoring include:
(a) Supervision, ie systematic direct observation of work and behaviour?
(b) Assessment of compliance with training, instructions, operating procedures?
(c) Inspection of samples of work in progress and completed?
(d) Monitoring the quality of this checking?
33 Does reactive monitoring include:
(a) A system for reporting incidents and near misses which involve isolation deficiencies?
(b) Incident investigation to determine both immediate and underlying management-related causes, including the adequacy of the installed isolation facilities and human factors?
(c) Communication through the organisation of lessons to be learned, and improvements to procedures to prevent recurrence?

### 5 AUDIT

Independent audits verify that the isolations systems are implemented and drive any remedial action.

34 Is an audit programme in place and implemented?
35 Are significant (positive and negative) results of audits communicated to 'controlling mind' level of the organisation?
36 Are action/improvement plans prepared and implemented?

### 6 REVIEW

The overall isolations systems are periodically reviewed.

37 Do senior managers review the overall isolation system at defined intervals against the policy objectives, taking information from monitoring and auditing activity?
38 Are the review mechanisms responsive to considering lessons from relevant industry incidents and to considering impacts of organisational change?

# Appendix 4: Valve types and issues

1 Table A outlines the characteristics of common valve types. Select isolation valves carefully to ensure successful performance in service, based on isolation circumstances. Key factors are:

- sealing ability;
- security (potential for accidental or deliberate reopening); and
- reliability (potential for partial or total loss of seal).

2 Limitations on the use, for isolation, of valves with other primary functions include:

- control or choke valves are not generally suitable for isolation;
- emergency isolation valves may be used for plant isolation, provided they are of a suitable type for the fluid and conditions being isolated;
- relief valves should not be used unless there is a purpose-designed method of securing the valve in the closed position **and** if it is possible to pressure test the valve to the maximum anticipated differential pressure in the direction of the applied pressure. Particular care is required to ensure proper reinstatement of relief valves to their required operating status and correct set pressure.

3 Valves are likely to provide a tight seal 'on demand' only where you select:

- an appropriate type of valve; and
- trim materials compatible with the process fluid conditions.

4 Valve selection should take account of accumulated experience of a particular valve/trim combination performing satisfactorily under specific process conditions.

5 Use commissioning tests to confirm the initial sealing performance of the installed valve.

6 Prove the leak tightness of a valve **every** time it is used for isolation.

7 Once a valve has been proven leak tight, the likelihood of a leak then developing during the isolation is low, but this could be an issue for long isolations (eg greater than a month). In such situations, consideration should be given to the periodic testing of the upstream valve of the isolation.

8 Careful consideration is required before using valves which provide a double seal in a single-valve body with a bleed in between (eg double-wedge gate, parallel expanding gate or double-seal ball valves) for isolation. In some applications, both barriers cannot be easily tested. Also, the security of the isolation depends upon the immobilisation of a single valve operating stem. Such valves should be used in preference to a double block and bleed isolation method **only after full consideration of these increased risks**.

| Valve type | Sealing ability | Security | Comment |
|---|---|---|---|
| Ball | Good | Physical disablement | ■ The optimum choice with regard to sealing ability, provided the valve body and trim materials are fully compatible with process conditions.<br>■ Generally set fully open or shut so sealing surfaces are not exposed to fluid flow – erosion damage is unlikely to be a problem.<br>■ Always disable physically due to easy valve operation. |
| Plug | Good | Physical disablement | |
| Butterfly | OK | Physical disablement | ■ Sealing surfaces are exposed to fluid flow therefore sealing ability is less certain.<br>■ Corrosion/erosion may be a problem as length of service increases.<br>■ A well-specified soft-seated valve is likely to seal better than a hard-faced valve.<br>■ Always disable physically due to easy valve operation. |
| Globe | OK | Tagging/admin controls may be acceptable | ■ Sealing surfaces are exposed to fluid flow so corrosion or erosion may occur after significant service.<br>■ Use for flow throttling increases the potential for erosion damage.<br>■ Where a valve is used for flow control, sealing problems should be anticipated after significant service.<br>■ Movement from shut to fully open requires many turns of the valve wheel – dependent on the hazard, tagging and administrative controls may provide adequate security. |
| Gate | OK | Tagging/admin controls may be acceptable | ■ Corrosion/erosion may be a problem in valves that have seen significant service as one of the sealing surfaces is exposed to fluid flow.<br>■ Not normally specified for flow control so more likely than a globe valve to provide a tight seal.<br>■ Movement from shut to fully open requires many turns of the valve wheel – dependent on the hazard, tagging and administrative controls may provide adequate security. |
| Screwdown non-return | OK | Tagging/admin controls may be acceptable | See comments for gate valves. |
| Needle | Variable | Tagging/admin controls may be acceptable | ■ Some are not designed to provide a tight seal, so suitability for isolation applications will depend on the actual valve.<br>■ Where the valve is capable of being fully shut, the comments for globe valves apply. |

**Table A:** Characteristics of common valve types. The isolation circumstances should always determine the valve selection

# Appendix 5: Isolation methods

1 Physical isolation of pressurised systems is primarily achieved using various combinations of valves, spades and blank flanges.

2 Pipelines often have long sections of pipe between valves. You may need to use techniques such as pipe plugs or pipe freezing to enable the isolation of intermediate sections of pipe for maintenance purposes, when it is not reasonably practicable to use primary devices (see Table B below). Such techniques are **not** appropriate for **standard** use on process plant and should be subject to task-specific risk assessment and senior-level authorisation.

3 A summary of isolation techniques is given in Table B. This indicates the key features and applications of each device.

**Table B:** Summary of isolation techniques

| Technique | Brief description | Typical use (process plant or pipelines) and pressure | Features – pros | Features – cons | Comments, refs to industry codes |
|---|---|---|---|---|---|
| Primary devices | | | | | |
| **Valves** | The simplest form of isolation device | ■ Standard use for process plant and pipelines<br>■ Suitable for all fluids at all pressure ranges | ■ Does not require intervention into the pipe – no significant hazard to the person performing isolation<br>■ Facility already installed, locations identified from P&IDs<br>■ Isolation is fast and removal to reinstate plant is easy<br>■ No specialist training or materials required<br>■ Continual attendance or monitoring not usually required<br>■ Low cost | ■ May not give tight shut-off due to seal damage<br>■ Positive indication of complete isolation is not always available, additional monitoring may be required<br>■ Requires locking off to prevent inadvertent operation<br>■ May not be in optimum position, resulting in large inventories beyond the isolation<br>■ Additional cost of valve and maintenance throughout the lifetime of the plant<br>■ Not all valve types are suitable for isolation use (Appendix 4) | Valves to be suitable for service fluid and rated to the maximum differential pressure<br><br>See:<br>ISO 14313[22] for pipeline valves<br>API 6D |

| Technique | Brief description | Typical use (process plant or pipelines) and pressure | Features – pros | Features – cons | Comments, refs to industry codes |
|---|---|---|---|---|---|
| Primary devices | | | | | |
| **Spades and spectacle plates** | A solid plate inserted between flanges<br><br>See Figure 8 | ■ Standard use for process plant and pipelines<br>■ Suitable for all fluids over a range of pressure ratings | ■ Positive isolation<br>■ Clear indication of presence<br>■ No specialist training or materials required<br>■ Continual attendance or monitoring not usually required<br>■ Low component cost | ■ Requires intrusion into the process to break and make joints<br>■ Requires temporary isolation for insertion and removal – such isolations may be remote from the worksite, making control more difficult<br>■ Relatively slow to install<br>■ Flanges may not be in optimum position, especially in welded pipework, resulting in large inventories beyond the isolation | Spades and spectacles to be compatible with the service fluid and rated to the maximum operating pressure<br><br>See notes for Figure 8 |

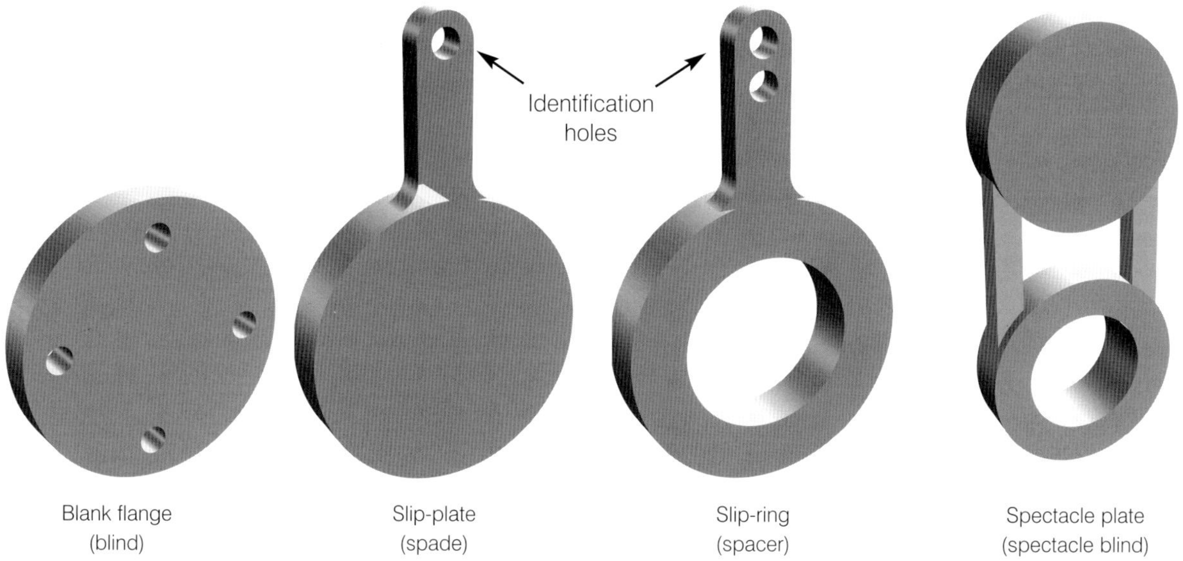

Identification holes

Blank flange (blind)

Slip-plate (spade)

Slip-ring (spacer)

Spectacle plate (spectacle blind)

**Figure 8:** Spades and spectacle plates

The size and material of spades and spectacle plates must be clearly marked, together with the class rating for which they are suitable. An unambiguous system should differentiate between slip-rings and spades, for example slip-rings have two holes on their tail while spades have one.
The condition and suitability of the spades and spectacle plates should be checked before each use. When not in use, they should be stored properly and separately.

| Technique | Brief description | Typical use (process plant or pipelines) and pressure | Features – pros | Features – cons | Comments, refs to industry codes |
|---|---|---|---|---|---|
| Primary devices | | | | | |
| **Physical dis-connection** | Remove spool and install blank flange (blind) | ■ Standard use for process plant and pipelines<br>■ Suitable for all fluids over a range of pressure ratings<br>■ Ideal for extended term, infrequent isolation | ■ Positive isolation<br>■ Indication of presence<br>■ Clear indication of even minor failure<br>■ No specialist training or materials required<br>■ Continual attendance or monitoring not usually required<br>■ Blank flanges can incorporate valves etc for bleeding/venting and monitoring purposes<br>■ Low component cost | ■ Requires intervention into the process to break and make joints<br>■ Requires temporary isolation for insertion and removal – such isolations may be remote from the worksite, making control more difficult<br>■ Care is needed when installing and removing blanks as pressure can build up behind them<br>■ Slow to install and reinstate<br>■ Flanges may not be in optimum position, especially in welded pipework, resulting in large inventories beyond the isolation | Blanks to be compatible with the service fluid and rated to the maximum operating pressure |
| Specialist techniques | | | | | |
| **Squeeze off** | Pipe is squeezed together to stop flow using a mechanical or hydraulic clamp | ■ Specialist technique – temporary isolation of low and medium pressure gas network polyethylene pipework | ■ Simple technique<br>■ Location of isolation flexible<br>■ Relatively cheap | ■ Only suitable for use on polyethylene pipework<br>■ Causes physical deformation hence further squeeze offs should not be carried out within specified limits along the same length of pipe<br>■ Low differential pressure technique | IGE/TD/3[23] |
| **Foam bagging** | Foam is injected into a semi-porous bag, previously inserted into the pipework | ■ Specialist technique – low and medium pressure gas network for cast iron, ductile iron and steel mains | ■ Can be used when insufficient room to carry out a conventional mains isolation<br>■ A useful means of flow – stopping tapered, vertical or non-standard diameter pipe<br>■ Can be inserted without decommissioning the pipeline<br>■ Low cost option for abandoning mains or services | ■ For permanent abandonment only – not suitable for temporary isolations<br>■ A second method of isolation must be used if the technique is to form a permanent isolation, eg end cap or blank<br>■ May require specialist equipment and training | IGE/TD/3[23] |

| Technique | Brief description | Typical use (process plant or pipelines) and pressure | Features – pros | Features – cons | Comments, refs to industry codes |
|---|---|---|---|---|---|
| Specialist techniques | | | | | |
| **Pipe plugs** | A single multi-seal plug or a number of plugs in combination<br><br>See Figure 9 | ■ Suitable for process plant and pipelines<br>■ Normally used for short-term isolations | ■ Can provide an effective leak-free barrier<br>■ Isolation scheme can comprise a single multi-seal plug or a number of plugs<br>■ Medium cost | ■ If used as primary isolation technique, sufficient redundancy and independence should exist within or between plugs so that failure of a part of the sealing system does not cause total loss of sealing capability<br>■ Care must be exercised to ensure correct fitment for the full duration of the isolation – continuous monitoring required<br>■ Requires open end to access pipeline – limited choice of location<br>■ If control lines are damaged, pipe plugs can get stuck within the pipe<br>■ Specialist technique, requires specific training | Pipe plugs must be suitable for use with the fluid and rated to the required pressure – consultation with manufacturer necessary |

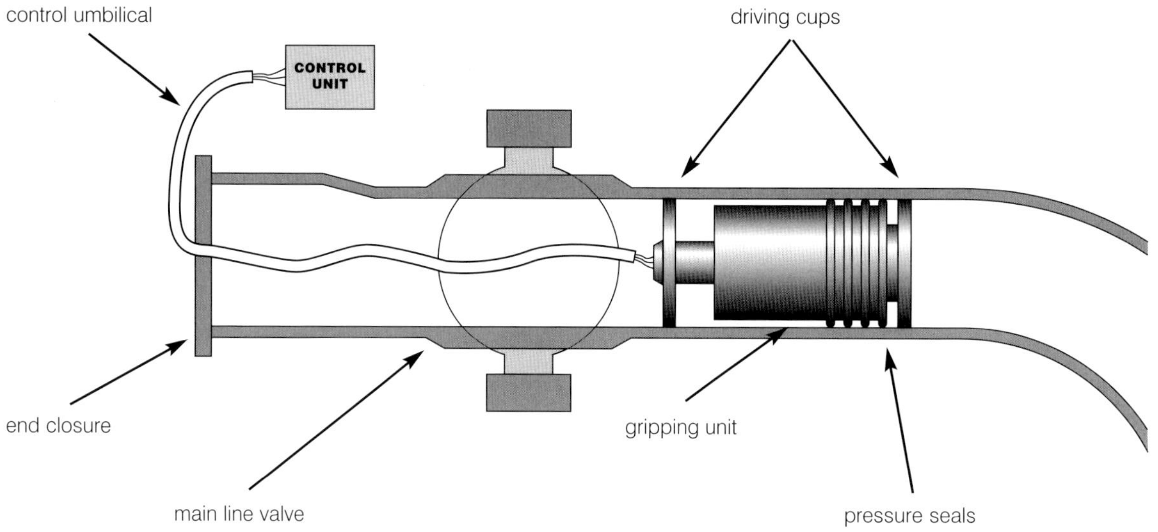

**Figure 9:** Pipeline plug

| Technique | Brief description | Typical use (process plant or pipelines) and pressure | Features – pros | Features – cons | Comments, refs to industry codes |
|---|---|---|---|---|---|
| Specialist techniques | | | | | |
| **Pipe stoppers** | A form of low differential pressure sealing plug | ■ Suitable for process plant and pipelines<br>■ Stoppers are primarily used as a secondary seal | ■ Simple to use<br>■ Low cost | ■ Not suitable as a primary isolation<br>■ Care must be exercised to ensure correct fitment for the full duration of the isolation – continuous monitoring required<br>■ Only suitable for low differential pressure isolations<br>■ Requires open end to access pipeline<br>■ No external indication of isolation | |
| **Inflatable bags** | Inflatable bag inserted through hole in pipe prior to being filled with air or nitrogen to effect a seal | ■ Suitable for use on low differential pressure isolation systems, eg low pressure gas pipelines<br>■ Used in pairs with a vent between bags or can be used singly as a secondary seal | ■ Inserted through relatively small holes cut into the pipe wall<br>■ Flexible location of isolation<br>■ Available in a large range of sizes<br>■ Allows flow of fluid to be maintained if a bypass is fitted<br>■ Pipeline does not need to be decommissioned<br>■ Medium cost | ■ Requires constant monitoring as bags can suddenly deflate and may be damaged when being installed through the cut hole or by swarf left in the pipe<br>■ Specific care must be taken when hot work is being undertaken close to an inflated bag isolation<br>■ Bag materials may be affected by some fluids (eg mercaptans)<br>■ Requires specialist equipment and trained personnel<br>■ Only suitable for low differential pressure isolations<br>■ Requires completion plugs to be fitted to pipelines | IGE/TD/3[23] |

| Technique | Brief description | Typical use (process plant or pipelines) and pressure | Features – pros | Features – cons | Comments, refs to industry codes |
|---|---|---|---|---|---|
| Specialist techniques | | | | | |
| **Hot tapping and stoppling** | Technique for plugging a pipe which is still subject to service pressure | ■ Suitable for use on most steel pipelines including sub-sea<br>■ Used to isolate a section of pipe and may allow continued operation by diverting the fluid through a temporary bypass | ■ Flexible location of isolation<br>■ Allows flow of fluid to be maintained if a bypass is fitted<br>■ Can be used on a wide range of diameters<br>■ Can be installed without decommissioning the pipeline | ■ Requires tee and other fittings to be welded onto pipe with high integrity welding and inspection<br>■ Requires careful control to prevent thermal build-up within the service fluid or interconnecting spaces<br>■ Not appropriate for systems containing chlorine, oxygen, hydrogen, hydrogen sulphide or hydrogen fluoride<br>■ Requires specialist equipment and trained personnel<br>■ Welded or bolted fittings and blanks remain on the pipeline<br>■ Relatively expensive technique | Welded fittings: BS 6990 *Code of practice for welding on steel pipelines containing process fluids or their residuals*[24]<br><br>See: IGE/TD/1 Ed 4[25] |
| **Pigs** | A dynamic isolation scheme that may be used to isolate a pipeline | ■ Suitable for pipelines<br>■ May be used in series separated by slugs of nitrogen, diesel, glycol, water (or a combination of inert fluids) to form a pig train | ■ Can withstand some differential pressure (a few bar) before train starts to move | ■ Requires specialist equipment and trained personnel<br>■ Relatively expensive technique<br><br>See Appendix 7 for other operational issues | |

| Technique | Brief description | Typical use (process plant or pipelines) and pressure | Features – pros | Features – cons | Comments, refs to industry codes |
|---|---|---|---|---|---|
| Specialist techniques | | | | | |
| **Pipe freezing** | Fluid within the pipe is frozen to form a solid plug. A coolant (solidified or liquefied gas) is used around the outside of the pipe wall | ■ Suitable for process plant and pipelines<br>■ Can be applied for:<br>- water-based service liquids (using carbon dioxide as coolant) and<br>- hydrocarbons, acids, alkalis, chlorides, ammonia, etc (using liquid nitrogen as coolant) | ■ Does not require intrusion into the pipework<br>■ Location of isolation flexible<br>■ Can be used on non-standard pipe diameters | ■ The plug may move/melt leading to failure of the isolation<br>■ Continual monitoring required<br>■ Pipe materials, joints and components can be adversely affected by the freezing operation<br>■ Failure to equalise the pressure across the plug can result in physical damage to the pipework – when the plug thaws it will be propelled along the pipe<br>■ Expense and complexity of technique varies, dependent on fluid, pipe diameter and flow rate<br>■ Specialist training required | |

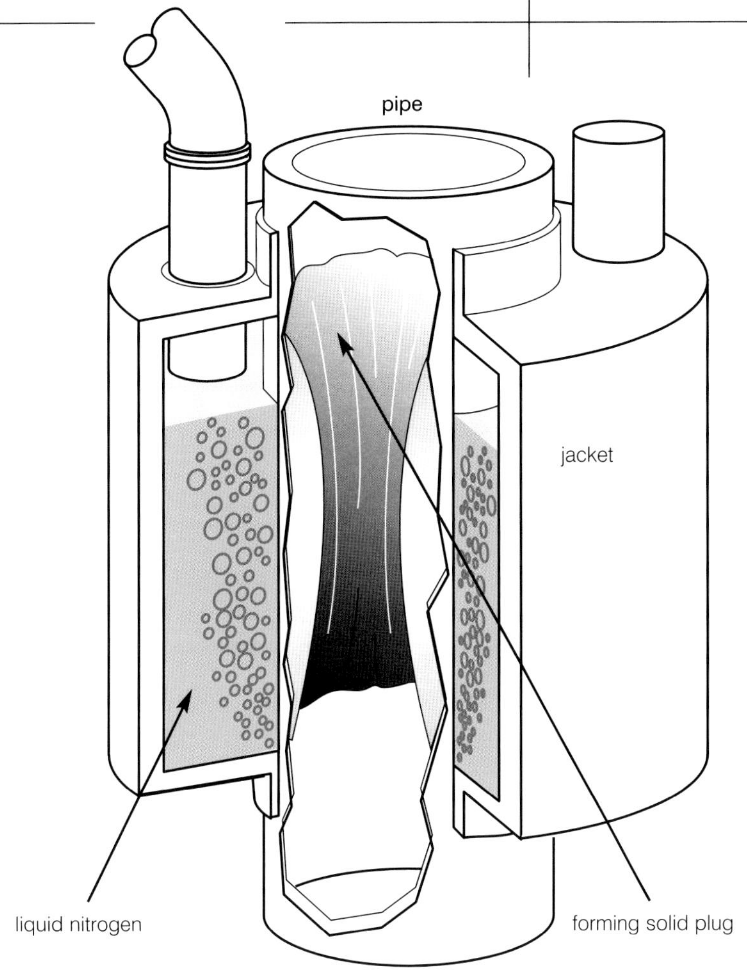

**Figure 10:** Pipeline freezing

# Appendix 6: Example of a selection tool to establish the 'baseline standard' for a final isolation

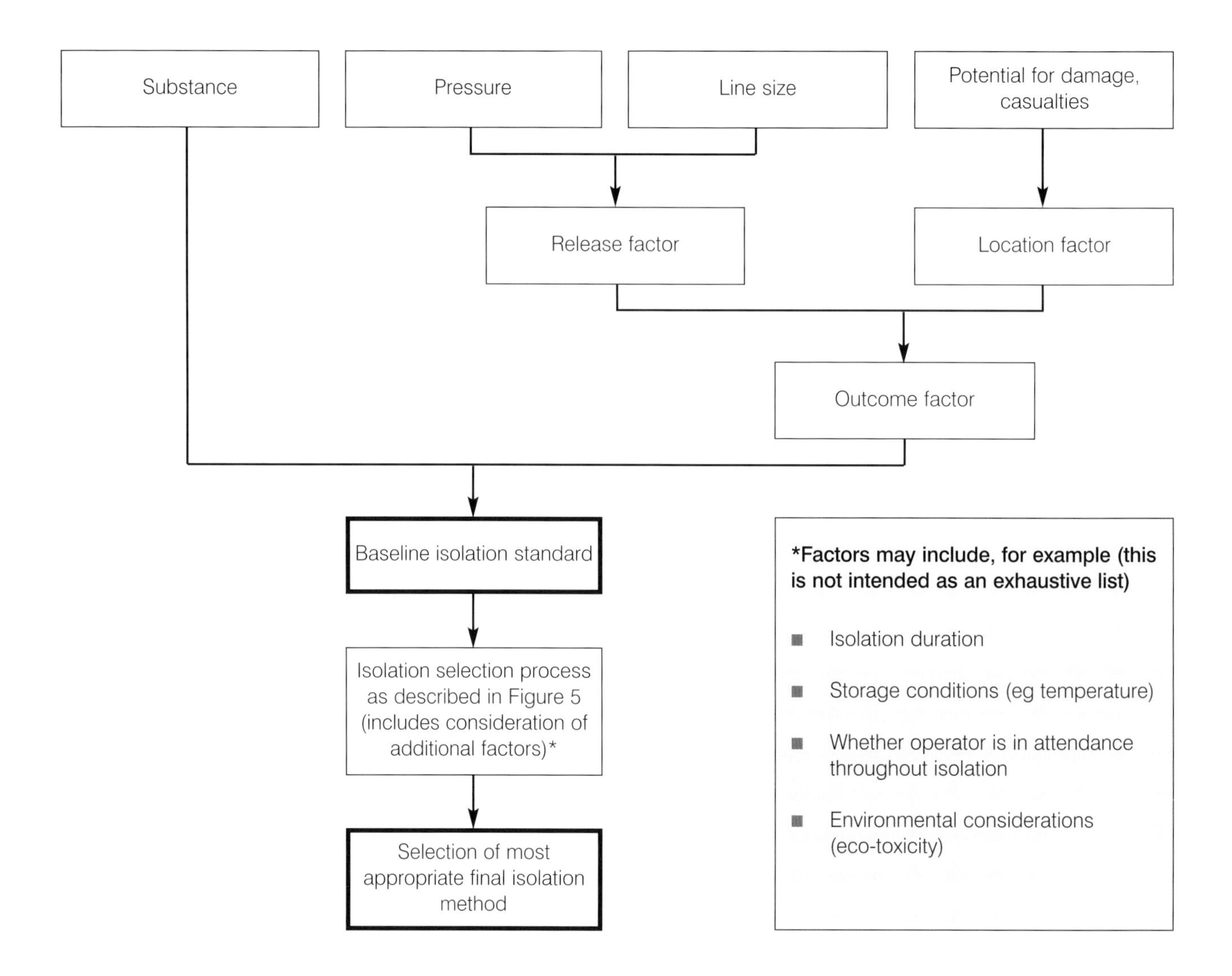


**Figure 11:** Overview of use of the selection tool to select a final isolation method

## Application of the selection tool

1 The tool is **not** intended to be used for:

- pipelines;
- extended term isolations; or
- 'high risk' situations eg;
  - confined space entry;
  - where the result of isolation failure could be catastrophic, or a situation from which recovery would be very difficult.

2 Before carrying out **any** isolation to enable intrusive work, ensure that you have minimised the risk associated with the task. You may be able to:

- shut down the relevant plant to enable work to be carried out safely, or postpone the job until the next planned shutdown;
- remove the need to break containment by using a different method to carry out the work; or
- minimise risk by other measures eg reduction of inventory and/or of the number of people exposed to risk.

3 Remember that a selection tool can complement, but cannot replace, competent technical judgement and common sense.

4 The tool has been calibrated against industry good practice for work on live plant. It gives a **baseline** isolation standard (provisionally the minimum acceptable standard for final isolation). This baseline standard is an input to the isolation selection process in Figure 5.

5 The tool is **not** designed to produce a final decision on the most appropriate final isolation standard and **must not be used in this way.** Full consideration of an individual isolation (including eg isolation duration, storage temperature, personal injury hazards etc) will be required to enable selection of the most appropriate final isolation standard.

## Substance category

6 Use the guidelines below to select the appropriate substance category, or categories, from the list in Table C. These are primarily (but **not** exclusively) based on the classifications given in the *Chemicals (Hazard Information and Packaging for Supply) Regulations 2005* (CHIP). CHIP substance classifications are given in the current version of the Approved Supply List[26] (ASL) to these regulations. For Table C, note that some categories (eg steam) are **not** based on CHIP classification.

7 Ensure that you identify all of the relevant categories for the substance to be isolated (eg flammable **and** toxic, or petroleum product **and** carcinogen). You should then assess each category and select the highest of the indicated isolation standards as your baseline standard.

8 For mixtures and preparations (including solutions), use the CHIP classification appropriate for the pure substance **unless either**:

- the substance entry in the ASL shows it to be:
  - within specified concentration limits such that an alternative classification applies (eg hydrogen sulphide, methanol); or
  - below its lower limit of concentration; or
- the substance is present at a level below the lower limit of concentration for the relevant classification, as given in Schedule 3 to the CHIP Regulations.[26]

9 Where substances are neither listed in Table C nor classified under CHIP, you should obtain specialist advice.

10 Remember that additional hazards may be associated with the storage conditions of unclassified fluids, eg hot water subject to gas pressure or capable of flashing to steam on release, cryogenic storage, gases stored under pressure. You should then consider defaulting to category 2.

11 Categories have been based on the potential for **harm to humans.** You may also need to take into account the potential for **environmental** damage.

12 If in doubt about the appropriate category to use, you should always err on the side of caution.

| Category | Description (CHIP classification, where appropriate) |
|---|---|
| 1 | Very toxic (T+)<br>Toxic (T)<br>Carcinogenic, mutagenic, toxic for reproduction<br>Sensitising |
| 2 | Extremely flammable (F+)<br>Highly flammable (F)<br>Flammable gases (R10)<br>Flammable liquids (R10) - unless included in category 4<br>Petroleum products* - unless included in category 4 - consider whether category 1 is appropriate<br>Oxidising (O)<br>Explosive (E)<br>Steam<br>Pressurised gases >250 bar.l, with pressure of 0.5 bar or higher<br>Flashing fluids<br>Asphyxiants |
| 3 | Corrosive (C)<br>Harmful (Xn)<br>Irritant (Xi) |
| 4 | Flammable liquids stored below flashpoint, and below flash point following release (R10) |
| 5 | Non-classified and not stored in a potentially harmful state |

**Table C:** Substance category

**Note:** * Petroleum substances are specified individually within category 2 because, for these substances, CHIP contains only a partial entry (ie classification for carcinogenicity only, not for flammability), as explained in note H to the *Approved Supply List*.[26] For the purposes of this selection tool, both flammability and carcinogenicity should be considered.

## Release factor

13 Combine line size and pressure to give a **release factor** (this reflects the potential rate of release). The options are high (H), medium (M) and low (L), as shown in Table D:

| | | **Pressure** | | |
|---|---|---|---|---|
| **Line size** | | >50 barg | ≤ 50 but >10 barg | <10 barg |
| | ≥ 20cm | H | H | M |
| | 5cm< line<20cm | H | M | L |
| | ≤ 5cm | M | L | L |

**Table D:** Release factor

## Location factor

14 Consideration of the location should include the potential for casualties (numbers at risk), escalation and damage if a release occurs. Take into account the nature of the possible consequences if the isolation fails, eg vapour cloud explosion (VCE), toxic gas cloud, jet fire with potential for escalation etc. The categories for **location factor** are again high (H), medium (M) and low (L), as defined in Table E:

| Category | Description |
|---|---|
| H | Any of:<br>Numbers at risk >10; congested equipment; potential for escalation; large fires with potential for damage and multiple fatalities |
| M | Typically:<br>3-10 at risk; uncongested plant, storage area or small number of items in open area; minor fire |
| L | Characterised by:<br>1-2 at risk; remote single items; easily contained minor fires |

**Table E:** Location factor

## Outcome factor

15 Combine the **release factor** and **location factor** to give an **outcome factor**, in the range A-C, as shown in Table F:

| | | Release factor | | |
|---|---|---|---|---|
| Location factor | | H | M | L |
| | H | A | B | B |
| | M | B | B | C |
| | L | B | C | C |

**Table F:** Outcome factor

## Determination of baseline isolation standard

16 The substance category and outcome factor are then combined to indicate the appropriate **baseline standard** for final isolation (Table G).

| | | Outcome factor | | |
|---|---|---|---|---|
| | | A | B | C |
| Substance category | 1 | R | I | I |
| | 2 | R | I | II |
| | 3 | I | II | II |
| | 4 | II | II | II |
| | 5 | II | III | III |

**Table G:** Baseline standard of isolation

Where:

R Consider whether the associated risk is acceptable or whether there is a need to further reduce risk by eg risk reduction measures, extending the isolation envelope, plant shutdown
I Positive isolation
II Proved isolation
III Non-proved isolation

17 Having identified the appropriate baseline standard, **full consideration** of an individual isolation will be required (see Figure 5) to enable selection of an appropriate final isolation standard. The baseline standard is based on consideration of major hazard risks – before selecting a final isolation method, you need to consider **all** relevant risks (including those due to eg personal injury hazards). You should document the basis for your selected final isolation standard as part of your assessment record.

18 If you cannot achieve the baseline standard of isolation, you may need to alter the method of work, postpone the job or implement additional measures. **Where an option is available which will further reduce risk, this should always be used.**

### Summary of considerations when using the selection tool

- It is not intended for use with:
  - pipelines;
  - 'high risk' situations (eg confined space entry);
  - extended term isolations.
- You should **always** challenge whether the output is compatible with common sense and professional judgement – particularly where input values lie close to category boundaries.
- Substance categories do not allow for all additional hazards associated with storage conditions – you may decide to default to a more hazardous substance category.
- If in doubt about the appropriate category to use (especially for substance category or location factor), you should err on the side of caution.
- The selection tool gives the **baseline** standard (usually this will be the minimum acceptable isolation standard). This is **not** always the most appropriate final isolation standard. You will need to ensure consideration of **all** relevant factors when selecting the final isolation.
- Use of a 'variation' (ie an isolation standard less than the baseline) may be acceptable in exceptional circumstances, eg for some short-term isolations.
- Record the basis for your decisions about isolation standards.
- The objective is not to meet/exceed the baseline standard, but to ensure that the risk associated with your isolation activity is both:
  - minimised to **ALARP**;
  - **tolerable**.

## Typical examples

A pump in benzene (toxic/flammable) service has a maximum operating pressure of 20 barg. The suction flange is 40 cm. If a release occurs there is significant potential for escalation.

Substance = 1, 2 (CHIP categorisation: F, Carc Cat 1, T)<br>
Release factor = H<br>
Location factor = H<br>
Outcome factor = A

Appropriate isolation standard: 1A = R<br>
2A = R

**Need for further consideration/risk assessment indicated. Conclusion may be eg that category I positive isolation is appropriate, or that it is not appropriate to work on live plant.**

A pump in hydrocarbon/hydrofluoric acid (toxic/flammable) service has a maximum operating pressure of 12 barg. The suction flange is 30 cm. The numbers at risk are >10 and there is significant potential for escalation.

Substance = 1 (CHIP categorisation T+, C), 2<br>
Release factor = H<br>
Location factor = H<br>
Outcome factor = A

Appropriate isolation standard: 1A = R<br>
2A = R

**Further consideration/risk assessment required. Conclusion likely to be either positive isolation or do not carry out work on live plant.**

A very high pressure (>100 barg) steam boiler circulating pump is occasionally isolated for maintenance. The suction flange is 30 cm. Congested equipment, >10 at risk.

Substance = 2<br>
Release factor = H<br>
Location factor = H<br>
Outcome factor = A

Appropriate isolation standard: 2A = R

**Need for further consideration/risk assessment indicated. In these circumstances the risk to workers may be such that work on live plant is inappropriate.**

A pump in liquid butane (LPG) service with a maximum operating pressure of 15 barg and suction line size of 10 cm is isolated for maintenance occasionally.

Substance = 2 (CHIP categorisation F+)<br>
Release factor = M<br>
Location factor = H<br>
Outcome factor = B

Appropriate isolation standard: 2B = I

**Baseline isolation is category I, positive isolation.**

A section of 25 cm fire water main (3 barg 'jockey' pressure) in a tank farm area (1-2 at risk) has to be isolated annually to change out some hydrant valves.

Substance = 5
Release factor = M
Location factor = L
Outcome factor = C

Appropriate isolation standard: 5C = III

**Baseline isolation is category III, single or double valve, no bleed.**

A section of an 20 cm steam line carrying superheated steam at 15 barg and 300ºC requires isolating to permit a branch to be welded into the line.

Substance = 2
Release factor = M
Location factor = M
Outcome factor = B

Appropriate isolation standard: 2B = I

**Baseline isolation is category I, positive isolation. Risk assessment may indicate that risk to workers is such that plant shutdown is appropriate.**

Isolation of a 10 cm gasoline line at 10 barg and 20ºC in a tank farm manifold where one or two workers might be present.

Substance = 2 (may also be category 1, depending on CHIP classification)
Release factor = L
Location factor = M
Outcome factor = C

Appropriate isolation standard: 2C = II
1C = I

**Baseline isolation is category I, positive isolation, or category II, proved isolation, depending on CHIP classification for carcinogenicity.**

Isolation of a 30 cm methane line at >50 barg for the overhaul of regulator equipment.

Substance - 2 (CHIP classification)
Release factor - H
Location factor - M
Outcome factor - B

Appropriate isolation standard: 2B = I

**Baseline isolation standard is positive isolation. Risk assessment may indicate that for short duration, manned operations it is appropriate to use proved isolation, with appropriate procedural controls.**

# Appendix 7: Pipeline isolation requirements

## General

1 The main methods for pipeline isolation are:

- the isolation and decommissioning of the entire pipeline, or pipeline system; or
- the isolation and decommissioning of a localised section of the pipeline.

**Note:** The isolation selection tool (Appendix 6) is not appropriate for the selection of pipeline isolations.

## Whole pipeline isolation

2 Isolation of a complete pipeline or pipeline system will normally be at the end points. This may involve existing isolation valves, spectacle blinds, removable spool pieces, etc. Procedures similar to those used for plant isolation may be used. However, for many pipeline applications, vents are left open to minimise the differential pressure across the downstream isolation barrier. When isolating sections of pipeline, you should consider the hazard from thermal expansion of liquid trapped in the section between isolation valves as this could result in line rupture.

## 'Localised' isolations

3 Localised isolation of pipelines can involve various isolation techniques or combinations, eg valves, removable spool pieces, pipe freezing, line plugging, pipe stoppers, bags, high friction pigs or spheres, use of 'slugs' of inert fluids and flooding sections of pipeline with water.

4 The technique used as the primary means of isolation may be backed-up, or supported, by a duplicate or alternative method, for example:

- a stopple as the primary means with bags as a secondary isolation barrier (with an open vent or drain in between); or
- high friction pigs as the primary means with pipe freezing as a secondary barrier.

5 You should consider whether the nature, risk, complexity and remoteness of the pipeline isolation are such that it is appropriate to carry out trials before applying the scheme at the worksite.

6 Ensure good communication schemes, particularly for isolation of long pipeline sections. It is vital to ensure that inadvertent de-isolation cannot take place at one end of a pipeline during work at the other end. Isolate prime movers, ie pumps and compressors, using locks or interlocks.

## Pipeline valves

7 When using valves for pipeline isolation, you should aim to achieve a double block and bleed isolation. See Figure 12.

8 Main line block valves may have bypass schemes around them to allow pressure equalisation, maintain pipeline flow during main valve isolation, etc. Where you use a main line valve for isolation, you should also shut down the bypass scheme and apply a comparable standard of isolation (ie double block and bleed isolation).

9 Pipeline emergency shutdown valves (ESDVs) required on offshore installations by regulation, ie the Pipelines Safety Regulations 1996,[27] may be used as part of an isolation scheme. However, they should **not** be used to control pipeline fluid flow during decommissioning or recommissioning of the pipeline.

## Cold cutting or drilling into pipelines

10 Before cutting or drilling any pipeline, you should ensure that no release of pipeline fluids, uncontrolled ignition or other unsafe condition can occur.

11 Where appropriate, the section of pipeline should be isolated, depressurised (by flaring, venting or draining) and purged or flushed. You should ensure that no hazardous fluid can enter the section of pipeline being worked on.

12 Consideration should be given to the potential for pipe-spring due to locked-in stress – the pipeline should be adequately supported and restrained around the point of cut to prevent this occurring.

13 When making a break in a pipeline, a temporary electrical continuity bond must be fitted across the intended break.

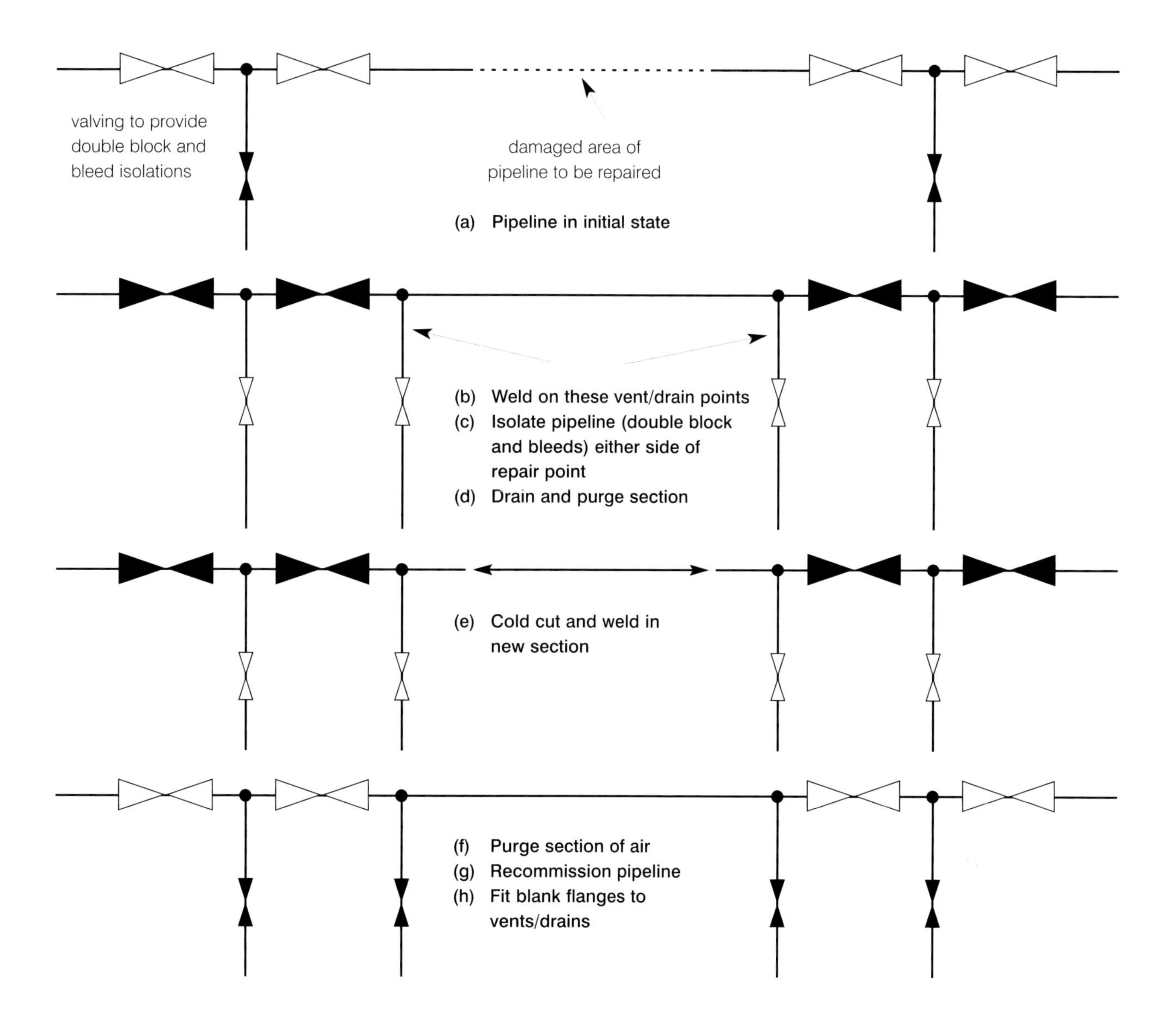


**Figure 12:** An example of an onshore pipeline repair using valves

## Isolation of pig traps

14 Pigging, and in particular pig trap isolation and opening the closure door to insert or remove a pig, is one of the more hazardous activities associated with operational pipelines. An example of a pig trap arrangement is shown in Figure 13 overleaf.

### *Pig trap main line isolation valves and bypasses*

15 Pig trap main line isolation valves are normally double seated gate or ball valves with a vent or drain point between the faces. This method of isolation is acceptable for normal pigging operations or routine maintenance activities.

16 Paragraph 153 in the main text discusses the use of actuated valves for isolation.

17 Any pig trap bypass (kicker) lines should be subject to a comparable standard of isolation as used for the main isolation valve.

### *Pig trap safety devices*

18 System interlocks and/or closure safety devices should be in place to prevent the closure door from opening before the trap has been isolated and depressurised.

19 You should have a means of indicating the pig trap internal pressure, preferably at two points – one near the closure door and the other near the main line isolation valve. All pressure indicators should be visible to those operating the closure mechanism.

20 The progress or location of the pig should be indicated (eg by using pig signallers). It is essential to know when the pig has left the pig trap or has been received in the trap, and its location within the barrel, before attempting to close main line isolation valves.

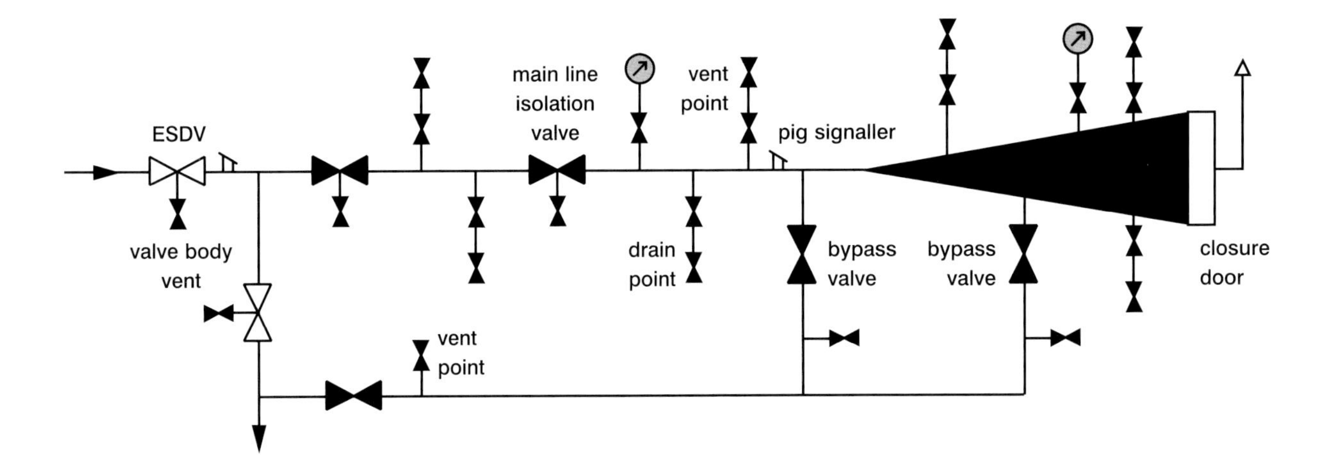


**Figure 13:** Pig trap main line isolation valves and bypasses

21 You need to be able to equalise the pressure on either side of a pig inside the trap, to prevent sudden and uncontrolled pig movement.

*Pig trap venting and draining*

22 It is essential to provide safe ways to vent and drain fluids from the pig trap. You need to consider two vent points and two drain points so that both sides of the pig can be drained, depressurised and purged, to prevent uncontrolled pig movement. Blockage of drain points can result from the build-up of debris in front of pigs. This could cause false indications of complete depressurisation. Your procedures should include measures to deal with this possibility.

*Pig loading and retrieval*

23 You should have equipment and procedures to enable removal of pigs without anyone having to enter the trap.

*Safety around pig trap closures*

24 Minimise the period of pig trap pressurisation. All workers should remain clear of the pig trap door in case of failure. Manually operated valves for pressurisation control should be sited well away from the door.

# Appendix 8: Draining, venting, purging and flushing activities

## Draining activities

1 Draining of liquids from process vessels and pipework may require a nominal pressure within the system to drive the liquid into a closed drains system. You may also need to pump or pig liquids out of a process system or pipework, or away from any section to be worked, eg using water, air or an inert substance. As part of a shutdown procedure, it may be possible to process out the majority of a vessel's contents via the normal process route, or to inject additives/cleaning chemicals to aid the removal of the fluid.

2 Issues which may need to be considered include:

- the asphyxiating effects of gases;
- volatile vapours given off from a liquid;
- formation of explosive atmospheres;
- protection of reception facilities from over-pressurisation or overfilling;
- vacuum effects within vessels/equipment during draining;
- the need to fully drain from valve cavities, 'dead-legs', valve pits and other confined spaces;
- disposal of pipeline fluids, contaminated water, etc;
- buoyancy effects if gas is used to displace liquids in underwater pipelines;
- compression effects leading to ignition of fluid vapours;
- blocking of drain points by debris;
- hydrostatic load on the pipeline/pipework.

## Bleeds and vents – hardware and operational issues

3 Use of bleed valves is discussed in paragraphs 178-179. Where bleeds used for depressurisation are routed to a closed disposal system, that system may be subject to variable back-pressures. Having depressurised the system, some small controllable venting facility to atmosphere, at a safe location, may be required to ensure that no pressure remains. When it is confirmed that no pressure is present, the work may proceed.

4 After venting or flaring, any vents that are connected to systems which may become pressurised, such as closed drains or flares, need to be closed to maintain the isolation envelope.

5 Bleeding and venting sequences should be designed to avoid trapped pressure or inventory within sections of equipment or plant, for example ball valve cavities. Isolation valves may have been installed with blanking plugs fitted to the body vent or drain points, which prevent the bleeding down of the valve body cavity. Extreme care is required if these plugs need to be removed and replaced with bleed valves while the pipeline is still in service, or if it is suspected that pressure is trapped within the valve cavity on a depressurised pipeline.

## Venting or flaring activities

6 Venting is the controlled depressurisation of a system by routing gas or vapour out of the system to a vent stack or into a flare header for disposal.

7 The following need to be considered when planning to vent or to flare off large volumes of gas from high pressure systems:

- flow rates should remain within the design capacity of the vent or flare;
- potential for hydrate formation, valve freezing or embrittlement effects on steel pipework (due to the Joule-Thomson effect); and
- associated noise level;
- flare consents.

8 Additional considerations for local venting operations include:

- the need to avoid all potential ignition sources (for example during periods of atmospheric electrical disturbance there should not be any venting);
- fitting earthing straps to prevent ignition of vented material by stray electrical currents or static electricity;
- the asphyxiating effects of vented gases;
- aircraft movement, particularly in the vicinity of installations where significant venting is possible; and
- gas dispersal or the formation of gas clouds. Gases heavier than air tend to accumulate at low points such as drains and tunnels. Ground-level gas clouds may form at or near populated areas. Atmospheric conditions may carry gas clouds a considerable distance from the point of venting.

## Purging activities

9 Purging is the continuous slug or cyclic filling and venting of a system with a gas or vapour (often inert, eg nitrogen) to clean/flush/displace hazardous substances.

10 Important considerations for any purging scheme include:

- the design limits of the system (temperature, pressure);
- the contents of the pressure system;
- the physical layout of the system or change in elevations (control the purge rate to ensure effective removal of system contents, taking special care to deal with low points and dead legs);
- potential for stratification or mixing effects between transported fluid and purge gas if purge rates are not properly controlled;
- Joule-Thomson effect problems with inert gas purging of volatile liquids;
- the asphyxiating effect of purge gases;
- the need to minimise the volume of toxic or flammable fluids released to the environment.

11 **Nitrogen** may be used to remove flammable gas. A correct purging sequence is vital ie flammable gas, nitrogen purge, test for any residual flammable gas, air purge. Use the reverse sequence on reinstatement. Vaporised, heated nitrogen under pressure can be effective in purging liquid-containing systems.

12 **Steam** is useful when heat is needed to aid the purging (eg with high boiling point substances) or to scour the surface of a vessel or pipeline. However, it can produce static electricity, so good earthing is needed. Expansion and condensation effects need to be considered, particularly when steaming fixed-roof storage tanks. Large vents will be needed to avoid damaging the tanks. Freezing of any condensate lodged in the system can block or fracture equipment.

13 **Air** may be used to purge non-flammable gases. It is unlikely to effectively remove all liquid from long pipelines/pipework systems. Some systems may be designed to allow the use of partial vacuum techniques. A final air purge may be required to ensure no asphyxiation hazard at a worksite.

14 Direct purging is a technique which is applicable to certain plant in the natural gas industry and involves the displacement of air by fuel gas or vice versa. Details of the technique and its application are found in the Institute of Gas Engineers Safety Recommendations IGE/SR/22 *Purging operations for fuel gases in transmission, distribution and storage*.[28]

## Flushing activities

15 Flushing is the continuous or cyclic filling and draining of the system with a liquid, such as water, to wash out hazardous substances.

16 Flushing can be important when:

- draining or venting could leave hazardous process residues trapped in less accessible parts of the plant (for example in internal fittings, instruments, dead-legs in pipework, valve-body cavities, legs and structures of floating roof tanks, roof fittings or vents, and on surfaces);
- process residues remaining within a plant could release trapped gases due to disturbance or changes in ambient temperature. High temperatures (eg from welding) may also cause chemical changes or ignition; or
- pipelines (eg off-plot chemical and oil installation) where hazardous residues can present particular problems are not amenable to pigging.

17 **Water** is often used for flushing, or to float out light substances from vessels. It is ideal for the removal of water-soluble materials, but is less effective for the removal of petroleum-type substances. Medium- or high-pressure water can be used to scour the surface of a vessel or pipeline. However, water must be totally removed from hot oil vessels because steam can be generated following recommissioning. In winter, freezing can cause blockages or equipment fractures. Water can increase corrosion risk, especially where the plant contains halogenated compounds. Pipework, pipework supports and vessels need to be designed to bear the weight if water-flushed. This is particularly important for large diameter systems that normally contain gases or low specific gravity liquids, eg flare systems.

18 Chemical solutions can be used to neutralise residual hazardous chemicals. A solvent or water flush may also be required.

# Appendix 9: Isolations for instrument work

1 The removal of instruments (sight glass, pressure gauge, level transmitter, etc) for repair or testing is one of the most common reasons for work on live plant containing hazardous substances. The principles for isolation of pressure systems can generally be applied to instrument isolation from the process system or pipeline. See paragraphs 132-136 and 189-196 in the main text. Typical instrument isolations are shown in Figure 14.

2 The isolation of an instrument may create problems such as unwanted control system actions when an instrument reading is absent and/or the loss of safety functionality while the work is carried out. Where loss of functionality is not self-revealing, you must be particularly careful to ensure the return of systems to their fully operational state on completion of the work.

3 Primary isolation valves should be located close to the pipe or vessel to which the connection is made and be to the same standard of pressure integrity. BS 6739: 1986 *Code of practice for instrumentation in process control systems: installation, design and practice*[29] contains guidance relevant to maintenance activity.

4 The instrument connections beyond the primary isolation facility may be less robust than the primary process connection. For example, compression fittings may be used in the impulse tubing installation and the instrument itself may include components such as flexible hoses or sight glasses. Your risk assessment should consider whether you need controls to limit inventory loss if the instrument system ruptures; these controls need to be carefully selected as malfunction can affect system functionality or reliability.

5 Most instruments have local isolation facilities to allow the instrument to be calibrated, function tested and maintained. These local isolation facilities, with the primary process isolation, can form a double block and bleed isolation.

6 Drain, vent and test points should have valves to close them off when not in use. These open connections should generally be plugged, but those removing the caps should be aware of the possibility of the risk of a pressure build-up from an undetected passing valve.

7 Plant of older design may have only a single valve, without a vent or drain, as the means of isolation. You should risk assess any such variations from your standards to establish the need for isolation facilities to be improved by plant modification (see paragraphs 137-140). Where instruments are mounted directly onto the vessel, and provide part of the primary process containment envelope, removal can be carried out only after isolation of the primary process vessel itself.

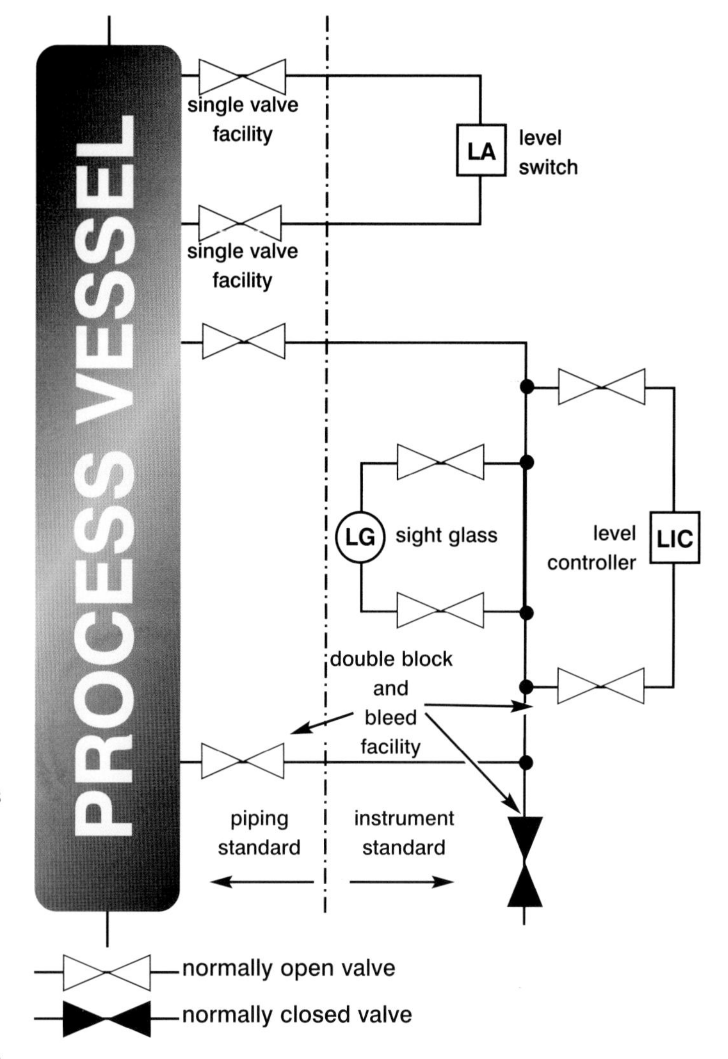


**Figure 14:** Typical instrument isolation arrangement

8 Proprietary equipment, such as some orifice plate carriers and corrosion monitoring access fittings, may allow removal of a plate or a coupon from a plant with only a single valve isolation. Such equipment should be operated in strict accordance with the manufacturer's instructions. Risk assessment will be needed to confirm that the standard of isolation provided is in line with the guidance outlined within this document. In any event, there should be separate means of isolating this type of equipment on both upstream and downstream sides.

# References and further reading


1 *Management of health and safety at work. Management of Health and Safety at Work Regulations 1999. Approved Code of Practice and guidance* L21 (Second edition) HSE Books 2000 ISBN 0 7176 2488 9

2 *The tolerability of risk from nuclear power stations* HSE Books 1992 ISBN 0 11 886368 1

3 *Successful health and safety management* HSG65 (Second edition) HSE Books 1997 ISBN 0 7176 1276 7

4 *Internal control: guidance for directors on the combined code* and *Implementing Turnbull: a boardroom briefing,* both published by the Institute of Chartered Accountants in England and Wales in 1999, are available at www.icaew.co.uk

5 *Safety signs and signals. The Health and Safety (Safety Signs and Signals) Regulations 1996. Guidance on Regulations* L64 HSE Books 1996 ISBN 0 7176 0870 0

6 *Safe use of work equipment. Provision and Use of Work Equipment Regulations 1998. Approved Code of Practice and guidance* L22 (Second edition) HSE Books 1998 ISBN 0 7176 1626 6

7 *Guidelines for the Management, Design, Installation and Maintenance of Small Bore Tubing Systems* EHS16 Institute of Petroleum 2000 ISBN 0 85293 275 8

8 BS EN 764-7: 2002 *Pressure equipment. Safety systems for unfired pressure vessels* British Standards Institution ISBN 0 580 39863 3

9 *Reducing error and influencing behaviour* HSG48 (Second edition) HSE Books 1999 ISBN 0 7176 2452 8

10 *Guidance on permit-to-work systems: A guide for the petroleum, chemical and allied industries* HSG250 HSE Books 2005 ISBN 0 7176 2943 0

11 *Manual handling. Manual Handling Operations Regulations 1992 (as amended). Guidance on Regulations* L23 (Third edition) HSE Books 2004 ISBN 0 7176 2823 X

12 *Control of substances hazardous to health (Fifth edition). The Control of Substances Hazardous to Health Regulations 2002 (as amended). Approved Code of Practice and guidance* L5 (Fifth edition) HSE Books 2005 ISBN 0 7176 2981 3

13 *Safe work in confined spaces. Confined Spaces Regulations 1997. Approved Code of Practice, Regulations and guidance* L101 HSE Books 1997 ISBN 0 7176 1405 0

14 *Safe maintenance, repair and cleaning procedures. Dangerous Substances and Explosive Atmospheres Regulations 2002. Approved Code of Practice and guidance* L137 HSE Books 2003 ISBN 0 7176 2202 9

15 *Remotely operated shutoff valves (ROSOVs) for emergency isolation of hazardous substances: Guidance on good practice* HSG244 HSE Books 2004 ISBN 0 7176 2803 5

16 *Guidelines for the Management of Integrity of Bolted Pipe Joints* EHS15 UKOOA 2002

17 *Memorandum of guidance on the Electricity at Work Regulations 1989* HSR25 HSE Books 1989 ISBN 0 11 883963 2

18 *Electricity at work: Safe working practices* HSG85 (Second edition) HSE Books 2003 ISBN 0 7176 2164 2

19 BS EN 60947: 1998 *Specification for low-voltage switchgear and controlgear* British Standards Institution ISBN 0 580 29155 3

20 *Work with ionising radiation. Ionising Radiations Regulations 1999. Approved Code of Practice and guidance* L121 HSE Books 2000 ISBN 0 7176 1746 7

21 *Electrostatics. Code of practice for the avoidance of hazards due to static electricity* PD CLC/TR 50404: 2003 ISBN 0 580 42225 9

22 *Petroleum and natural gas industries – pipeline transportation systems – pipeline valves* ISO 14313: 1999 International Organisation for Standardisation

23 Institute of Gas Engineers IGE/TD/3 Edition 4 (1677) *Steel and PPE pipelines for gas Distribution* 2003

24 BS 6990: 1989 *Code of practice for welding on steel pipes containing process fluids or their residuals* British Standards Institution ISBN 0 580 16672 4

25 Institute of Gas Engineers IGE/TD/1 Edition 4 (1670) *Steel pipelines for high pressure gas transmission* 2001

26 *Approved Supply List. Information approved for the classification and labelling of substances and preparations dangerous for supply. Chemicals (Hazard Information and Packaging for Supply) Regulations 2005*. Approved List L42 (Eighth edition) HSE Books 2002 ISBN 0 7176 6138 5

27 *Pipelines Safety Regulations* 1996 SI 1996/825 The Stationery Office 1996 ISBN 0 11 054374 4

28 Institute of Gas Engineers IGE/SR/22 (1625) *Purging operations for fuel gases in transmission, distribution and storage* 1999

29 BS 6739: 1986 *Code of practice for instrumentation in process control systems: installation, design and practice* British Standards Institution ISBN 0 580 15295 2

## Further reading

Institution of Gas Engineers IGE/SR/23 (1623) *Venting of natural gas* 2000

*Dangerous maintenance: A study of maintenance accidents and how to prevent them* HSE Books 1992 ISBN 0 11 886347 9

*Personal protective equipment at work (Second edition). Personal Protective Equipment at Work Regulations 1992. Guidance on Regulations (as amended)* L25 (Second edition) HSE Books 2005 ISBN 0 7176 6139 3

*Safe use of lifting equipment. Lifting Operations and Lifting Equipment Regulations 1998. Approved Code of Practice and guidance* L113 HSE Books 1998 ISBN 0 7176 1628 2

## Further information

HSE priced and free publications are available by mail order from HSE Books, PO Box 1999, Sudbury, Suffolk CO10 2WA Tel: 01787 881165 Fax: 01787 313995 Website: www.hsebooks.co.uk (HSE priced publications are also available from bookshops and free leaflets can be downloaded from HSE's website: www.hse.gov.uk.)

For information about health and safety ring HSE's Infoline Tel: 0845 345 0055 Fax: 0845 408 9566 Textphone: 0845 408 9577 e-mail: hse.infoline@natbrit.com or write to HSE Information Services, Caerphilly Business Park, Caerphilly CF83 3GG.

British Standards are available from BSI Customer Services, 389 Chiswick High Road, London W4 4AL
Tel: 020 8996 9001 Fax: 020 8996 7001
e-mail: cservices@bsi-global.com
Website: www.bsi-global.com

The Stationery Office publications are available from The Stationery Office, PO Box 29, Norwich NR3 1GN
Tel: 0870 600 5522 Fax: 0870 600 5533
e-mail: customer.services@tso.co.uk
Website: www.tso.co.uk (They are also available from bookshops.)

# Glossary

**baseline isolation standard** the minimum acceptable standard of final isolation applied under normal circumstances. This standard is based on risk assessment. It can be determined using the methodology in Appendix 6 or by other means.

**blank flange (blind)** a component for closing an open end of pipework, which is suitably rated to maintain the pressure rating of the pipe and of an appropriate material to withstand the contents of the line.

**bleed or vent valve** a valve for draining liquids or venting gas from a pressurised system.

**block valve** a valve which provides a tight shut-off for isolation purposes.

**double block and bleed (DBB)** an isolation method consisting of an arrangement of two block valves with a bleed valve located in between.

**double-seated valve** a valve which has two separate pressure seals within a single valve body. It is designed to hold pressure from either direction (as opposed to a single seated valve). It may include a body vent between seals to provide a block and bleed facility.

**extended isolation** isolation which is to remain in place for more than three months.

**fluid** freely moving substance. Includes liquids and gases.

**hazardous substance** a substance which is able to cause harm or damage if loss of containment occurs. In some cases (eg water) the specific situation determines whether the substance belongs within this category.

**intolerable risk** risk at an unacceptably high level. Until the risk has been reduced, activity should not be started (or continued). If the risk cannot be reduced, even with unlimited resources, the proposed activity should not go ahead.

**isolating authority** person authorised to approve proposed isolations.

**isolation** the separation of plant and equipment from every source of energy (pressure, electrical and mechanical) in such a way that the separation is secure.

**isolation envelope** that part of the pipework system which is within the isolation points forming the boundary within which intrusive work can be performed. Where a valved isolation allows a physical isolation to be effected, it is the physical isolation point that forms the boundary of the isolation envelope.

**isolation scheme** a system incorporating three key components – management arrangements, risk control procedures and working-level practices, to ensure hazardous substances are not released nor people exposed to risks to their health and safety during the maintenance or repair of process plant or pipelines.

**own isolation** isolation where the same person both installs the isolation and carries out the intrusive work. Such isolations may be carried out under PTW or procedural control.

**permit-to-work (PTW)** a formal written system used to control certain types of work which are hazardous.

**pig** a device that can be driven through a pipeline by means of fluid pressure for purposes such as cleaning, dewatering, inspecting, measuring, etc.

**physical disconnection** a method of positive isolation where an air gap between the energy source and the plant/equipment is provided.

**pipeline** cross-country, offshore and pipelines within sites, for example, storage sites, and petrochemical plant. This guidance uses the definition of 'pipeline' given in BS EN 14161 ie 'the facilities through which fluids are conveyed, including pipe, pig traps, components and appurtenances, up to, and including the isolation valves'. However, pipeline installations such as compressor stations and pressure-regulating installations are not included in this definition – these are considered separately. Note that this differs from the legal definition of 'pipeline' within the Pipelines Safety Regulations 1996 (PSR) which includes certain pipeline installations, eg for gas pressure regulation. The relevant gas industry code for high pressure steel transmission pipelines is IGE/TD/1 and for distribution mains it is IGE/TD/3.

**pipeline installation** installations such as pressure regulating installations, compressor stations which, together with the pipeline itself, comprise a pipeline system (as defined in BS EN 14161). The relevant gas industry code for pressure regulating installations is IGE/TD/13.

**pipework** piping interconnecting items of process plant.

**piping and instrumentation diagram (P&ID)** schematic drawing defining the extent of equipment, piping and piping components and instrumentation.

**positive isolation** complete separation of the plant/ equipment to be worked on from other parts of the system.

**pressurised plant** facilities containing liquid or gases under pressure for treatment, processing or storage.

**proved isolation** valved isolation where effectiveness of the isolation can be confirmed via vent/bleed points before breaking into system.

**short-duration work** work which does not extend beyond one operating shift.

**slip-ring** a spacer ring installed in pipework to facilitate the insertion of a spade.

**spade (slip-plate)** a solid plate for insertion in pipework to secure an isolation. The spade must be of an appropriate material to withstand the line contents.

**spared equipment** equipment which is available to replace on-line equipment, eg during maintenance or in the event of breakdown.

**spectacle plate** a combined spade and slip-ring.

**tagging** temporary means of identifying a valve or other piece of plant.

**variation** a situation where circumstances require the use of an isolation of a standard lower than the baseline isolation standard (or where relevant, the established company standard). Use of a variation is acceptable only when it is supported by a situation-specific risk assessment. Variations must be appropriately authorised and fully recorded.

# Index

**Note:** where topics are listed in bold, they are defined in the glossary

Printed and published by the Health and Safety Executive 01/06 C45